# TALES
# OF THE
# OAK

WRITTEN AND PUBLISHED BY
MAGIC TORCH

Published by Magic Torch

ISBN 0-9539065-0-7

Printed by Compass QuickPrint, Greenock

First published October 2000

Woodcuts designed by Ross Ahlfeld
and handcrafted by Eddie O'Donnell
of Neil Street Community Workshops

Photography by David Goldthorp

All original artwork by Ross Ahlfeld

Monarch of the Woods, Land of the Strangers,
The Wizard and His King, Last Lord of the West,
The Tower, Last Orders, Dance with the De'il
written by Neil Bristow

St Fillans Fayre, Walking to the Kirk,
The Orchard, Market Cross, Night Watch,
Legacy of Para Handy, Restoration
and all poetry*
written by Paul Bristow

The Sun and the Hunter, The Duchal Ghost,
Cold Heart, Little Drummer Boy, Kidd's Tale,
The Mysterious Mystery of the Langhouse Ghost
written by Ray Mitchell

The Serpent and The Saint, Passing of the Torch
and all factual material
written by Magic Torch

"The Serpent and the Saint" originally appeared in a somewhat different
format in "Tall Ships Short Stories" published by
Greenock Tall Ships 1999.

Every effort has been made to contact the relevant sources
for permission for use of all other artwork.

Magic Torch, The Westburn Centre, 175 Dalrymple Street, Greenock, Scotland
email - magictorchgroup@hotmail.com

*with exception of the Auld Dunrod poems, Wulf and Eadwacer and The Green Oak Tree ,
which are traditional

"The legends represent the imagination of the country,
they are the kind of history which a nation desires to
possess. They betray the ambitions and ideals of the people,
and in this respect, have a value far beyond the tale of
actual events and duly recorded deeds which are
no more history than a skeleton is a man."

Standish O'Grady 1832-1915

"This old grey town, this firth, this further strand -
is world enough for me."

John Davidson "Ballad of the Making of a Poet"

# Foreword

Technically, Magic Torch are an "arts group". When we filled in the grant application for the "Awards For All" scheme, that's the box we ticked. And then we got the money to print the book, and suddenly it was like somebody else must have *believed* we were an arts group. Which just seemed so serious.

Everything we were doing with our writing and artwork was more of a lifestyle choice than anything else; if we heard a story about somewhere interesting, we'd drive to find it, maybe camp there, take photos, get a feel for the place. Have a laugh. Later on we'd do the work.

We live in this hugely cultural community, birthplace of writers, artists, playwrights, comedians. But what's more important than the tag we attach to someone is recognising that they are Just People. Sometimes that gets lost, and what becomes important is the Art with a capital "A", *not* the people. That might be one of the things that turns folk off. Art isn't, or shouldn't be exclusive, practised and appreciated by a select few: it is for everyone. And it is for everyone to do.

During the time we have spent working on Tales of the Oak, we have also had the chance to work on related community projects; an illuminated manuscript commemorating the history of the town which was put together for the Tall Ships celebrations; a folklore display at Cornalees Visitor Centre. For each of these projects, we involved as many other local folk as possible; we had schoolchildren from Gourock Primary designing us Celtic Borders, Eddie O'Donnell at Neil Street Workshops carving us traditional woodcuts, our old English teacher Gerry McGinty recording a reading of "The Ballad of Auld Dunrod" and an enormous diversity of people from Inverclyde Volunteer Centre tearing apart a room at Cornalees Visitor Centre and then rebuilding it to our designs. No one involved made *any* money from these projects, a genuine case of "art for art's sake".

And it is in working with all these people and the many more we haven't mentioned, that Magic Torch have come to believe in the philosophy that there is no such thing as "god given talent", there is only opportunity. We have had the *opportunity* to put this book together.

And if we can do it, then anyone can really.

Tick whatever box you like.

Magic Torch
July 2000

**Ross**

For my wife Jane, the girl who used to pass by me on the bus
- and for Granda Haggerty. He loved to draw and walk the cut;
he would have liked this.


**Neil**

For mum and dad, in memory of the hours
spent reading to me as a child.
Thank you for opening my eyes to the wonders of books.


**Paul**

In memory of my gran Sadie, who not only told me stories,
but loaned me her typewriter so I could start writing my own.


**Ray**

To the shipyard workers of the Clyde - and especially to my father,
Billy Mitchell. He built until there was nothing left to build; the river and
the iron run in his veins still.


And all of Magic Torch would especially like to dedicate"Tales of the
Oak"
to a new wee branch of the Green Oak tree,
Jayne Catherine Rice, born 9th August 2000

# CONTENTS

# Monarch of the Woods

*In the days when the earth was young, two lovers incur the wrath of their God and the quest for a sacred seedling reveals the origin of Greenock's name.*

Now there are many tales told of how Greenock came by its name. Some say that it comes from a great green oak tree which used to stand down by the shore in days gone by. Others say that in the old language, the word means sunny knoll or bay. For these tales, I cannot vouch. Instead I will tell you a *different* story, one that I have heard of how it was that Greenock came by its name. Doubtless it will raise many an eyebrow and as many a question, but I shall tell it just the same. It begins long ago when the earth was still young. Now in those days, he that made the world and everything in it was known to the people as Grannu, and he watched over all his creations and loved them very much.

At this time Grannu often walked on the earth that he loved so much, and of all things dearest to him after man was the great forests and all who dwelt in them. And so he decided to create a great woodsman, a hunter, someone who could tend to the many trees which covered the land of the west and all the beasts and birds which called them home. So he went to the sacred oak, the great tree which grew in the centre of the forest and he took down a branch. From this Grannu fashioned his new servant in the likeness of a man, and he named this mighty hunter Lorne, and made him protector of all the lands around the great river, where he was to ensure the balance. No creature would be too numerous, no seedling would surpass others. And Grannu said to him

"You are Lorne of The Trees. You are the ancient Oak, the sapling new and the seed untouched. You are the Raven nesting and the Wolf hunting. You are the roots of all and all living things are your branches. All you teach shall flourish and grow in the minds of men until autumn finally comes and the leaves fall and wither in preparation for the fallowness."

And so it was that any blow served on Lorne was a blow served on the very forest itself.

Great was his skill and never was an animal beyond his trapping, although he was careful not to take more than his share, and when he did it went to those who needed it most. He was as mighty as Oak, yet as gentle as a breeze blowing through its branches, and all who met him said there was never a kinder man than he, nor a wiser one. So it was that a great harmony fell upon the land of the west, and all living things pronounced him King of the trees, Monarch of the woods.

Long would he wander the great forest of the west, tending to the trees and all who made them their home, and many a tale is told of Lorne and

the great deeds done in those years. Then one day in summer, Lorne was walking in the great forest of Creagnamfiach, which we call Ravenscraig, when he came across a clearing in which sat a maiden of such beauty as the hunter had never seen. With a pale face and bright blue eyes, clad all in silver and white, with a chain of pearls and shells round her neck, she sat sobbing neath a great tree in the centre of the clearing.

"Why are thou unhappy fair maiden." asked Lorne as he entered the clearing.

"I have lost my way in these woods and have no way of reaching home before nightfall." answered the maiden.

"Pray tell, what is thy name?"

"I am Clutha, and I come from the banks of the great river."

Lorne looked upon the beautiful girl and smiled.

"Then come, let ye not waste another tear for we shall get you back to those banks ere night falls."

And so they journeyed on the secret paths that only Lorne knew and as the sun began to dip below the hills and Grannu took leave of the world for that day, they reached the edge of the forest and before them lay rolling fields and the banks of the great river.

"Here I am sorry to say, we must part. But before I return home I must know how can I repay you for your kindness Lorne the hunter."

"All I would ask of you my Lady Clutha is that you come and visit me in the forest tomorrow. I will leave a trail of acorns for you to follow, and at the end of them you shall find me waiting. Say you will come?"

"I will come." answered Clutha. And at that she set of across the fields to the crescent bay and her home there.

The Lady Clutha did visit Lorne the next day, and the day after, and the day after that. For three new moons she visited him every day, spending all their time together in that clearing where they had first meet. And there where she had shed those tears of sorrow, grew a new sapling undeterred by the onset of winter or the shadow of the great tree. And as it blossomed so too did their love. So it came to pass that as the leaves began to fall, Lorne and Clutha desired to be married. Word of this was quick to come to Grannu's ear, for he has many messengers in many forms. But whether it was bird or mammal, sprite of fairy who brought him the news that angered him so, this tale doesn't tell. Yet he learned of it all the same, and in time he came to speak with his woodsman and spoke to him thus.

"Lorne of the trees, I have heard that you plan to marry the Lady Clutha, she who dwells by the crescent bay. Is this true?"

"Aye my lord, it is." answered the hunter.

"But surely you know that this cannot be, for she is a child of the river,

married to the sea, and you my mighty woodsman, you are born of the trees to do my bidding and serve the land."

"But I love her."

"It matters not." said Grannu. "You are my woodsman, created to do my bidding, and I forbid it."

At this the Lord of the Trees was consumed with sorrow. He did not want to disobey his creator, yet he loved the Lady Clutha with all his heart. And so he decided that he would marry Clutha in secret and thus one night late in autumn, Lorne of the trees and fair Clutha exchanged wedding bands neath the great tree where they had first met. Much joy was in the heart of the two young lovers and as was the custom, they exchanged tokens of their affections. For Clutha, Lorne brought a silver acorn from the great tree, and in return Clutha presented Lorne with a silver sea shell. All living things took joy in their union, and as night fell the forest was full of celebration.

Yet as morning broke Grannu himself in the clearing where the two lay sleeping, and some say the anger was such that it set the whole forest and the lands beyond alight.

"Awake now, Lorne and Clutha, you who dare to marry without your God's blessing."

The great voice of Grannu woke the two lovers and greeted them with such angry and despite their pleads for forgiveness, was wont to judge them harshly, too harshly some have said. For he spoke onto them thus: "Impatient were you both for love. Thus it shall be your punishment to wait for it for eternity and a day. Till then you shall be banished to the realms of my choosing. Lorne, forever shall you remain in these woods, a tormented spirit of the trees. Clutha, to the depths of the cold river I send thee, forever to watch over the creatures of the sea, a bitter punishment for the bitter lover you are to become. Forever shall you be in sight of each other, but forever out of reach, tormented by the prospect of an impossible union. In this you shall learn the error of your ways."

From that day forth land and sea were parted and Lorne and Clutha were never to be together again. But it is not here in sorrow that our tale ends. For unknown to Grannu, Clutha carried with her to the depths of the river, the child of Lorne in her womb. When the child was finally born, Clutha entrusted him to the mermaids, with whom he would remain a baby until such a time as he was ready to leave the sea. But the lord of the trees knew nothing of this and for many a moon Lorne wandered through Birch and Oak, a solitary King with no queen, doomed to rule a lonely Kingdom. A great sadness came upon the Lord of the trees, he that was friend to bird and beast alike, a sadness which gave way to anger. The birds flew

from their nests, the wolves ran from their dens.  And in his anger, Lorne took up his axe and struck a mighty blow to the great tree, that which was so sacred to Grannu, cutting deep at its very roots, causing it to wither and die.  Yet in his rage, the Monarch of the woods had forgotten that every blow struck to the forest, was a blow struck to him, and thus as his great axe met with the sacred tree, he himself felt the force of it and he fell down in pain. Now was the time when a great sleep came upon him, a sleep that would last for years too numerous to count.

In this time darkness fell upon the once beautiful Oaks which Lorne tended, and a terrible sadness grew in the hearts of all living things.  The people were plagued by the famine and drought, believed their god had forsaken them and a great shadow was cast on the land. Many turned from Grannu and the old ways and all guise of civilised nature was cast aside. And then finally. after many moons, the hope of spring began to appear and Grannu once more turned his eye to the great forest. Saddened by the desolate shells of the once mighty oaks, he sent forth a great storm to wake his woodsman. The ground shook, the lightning flashed, and the sky cracked with a force greater than any ever known. And then silence.

The lord of forest had returned, and as he spoke, even the wind paused to listen.

"I am Lorne of The Trees. I am the ancient Oak, the sapling new and the seed untouched. I am the Raven nesting and the Wolf hunting. I am the roots of all and you are my branches. All I teach shall flourish and grow in the minds of men until autumn finally comes and my leaves fall and wither in preparation for the fallowness."

And these words were heard by all living things, and all took heart that he who was friend to beast and bird alike had *not* forsaken them.  The great tree had died and the forest withered with it, and little remained of the great oaks that Lorne had tended in his youth. And so he resolved to redress the balance, hoping that Grannu might find it in his heart to forgive him.

Yet without a seedling from the great oak the forest would forever remain barren, and Lorne did not now where one might be found.

So he asked the salmon, but he did not know. " ask the wolf who hunts so well. In all his wanderings perhaps he has seen that which you seek."

So he asked the wolf, and he did not know. "ask the raven who flies so high. With such a view perhaps he has seen that which you seek."

So he asked the Raven who answered him thus.

"I have seen that which you seek. As gold as the sun it glitters, in a crack as dark as night."

"Show me the way." commanded the great hunter.

And at his bidding, the Raven guided the Lord of the Trees across moor and peak, through vale wood and vale, until they came to the a dark chasm which scratched the land, laying open the world beneath. And it was into this pit that Lorne had to journey.

The sky cracked with thunder as the great hunter descended into those hollow hills, a flaming torch lighting his way. Long did he wander there in the darkness, and much mischief was caused him by the little folk who dwelt there. But in time he came to a grotto, with walls as green as emeralds, and there he found what he sought...an acorn of solid gold. This was the seedling of the great tree, placed there by the little folk for safe keeping in the days of darkness when Lorne slept his great sleep.

And this he took to a hill beyond the forest, overlooking the great river, taking great care in its planting. The seed took root quicker than any of a normal tree, yet it did not produce more than a thin sapling. Every day the hunter would tend to it, yet it still remained weak, and with it so too did the forest. Then one day, Lorne heard singing, the like of which he had never heard before, and drawn on to find its source he arrived at the crescent bay neath the ancient stone. And here he found a mermaid who carried in her arms a child.

"Who are you maiden of the sea, whose song is so sweet and so sad?" asked the great hunter.

"Do you not recognise me Lorne of the trees?" asked the mermaid.

And to this the hunter shook his head.

"I am the Lady Clutha of the river and all that flows is my domain. I am the herring swimming free, live giving water, mother of all. I am the river wide, the stream flowing and the raindrop falling. And this babe in my arms is your son, he that will heal the last of the wounds. Take him, and care for him with all your heart, for he is the true child of land and sea. Fare thee well my love."

And then she handed Lorne the child, wrapped as he was in a white shawl. "Clutha..." but the maiden had already disappeared beneath the waves. Forever in his sight, but always out of reach, she was lost to him now. And looking down at the child he saw that in it's hands it grasped a silver acorn, Lorne's gift to his wife on their wedding day. And then he knew what he must do.

So he took the silver acorn to the hill, and planted it opposite the golden one. Just as before it quickly took root, and as it grew, so do did the other sapling, each making the other stronger. And to these Lorne tended every day, and within a month two mighty oaks stood proud and tall atop that hill. In the years that followed, father and son restored the forest to good health, and happiness returned to the land of the west. And then in time, the son of Lorne, who had learned much from his father, left the forest to

live amongst the people of the river. And to them he taught many things, and they named him, Druman, their word for wise, for this he surely was.

And so it came to pass that a great grove of oaks took root on that hill, a gift from Clutha of the river and Lorne of the woods to their Lord Grannu. Thus in the days that followed that place became known to the Clann Abhainn Cluaidh, as the Grain Chnox, the Knoll of the sun, and it is said that Grannu so favoured the sacred Oaks that grew there that he never allowed them to lie in the shade at any hour of the day. Here that Lorne would often come, just in sight of the one he loved, but destined to be apart from her.
And so ends the tale of how Greenock came to find its name.

Epilogue - Of The Chronicles of the Clann Abhainn Cluaidh

As beauty returned to the land, the streams flowed fast and the trees grew tall. And for a time, peace was bestowed on the children of Lorne and Clutha, and their descendants grew large in number, multiplying and spreading far over all the lands of the west. But close to their heart did they keep that grove of Oaks so favoured by Grannu and often would they return there. And some say that a branch was cut from each of the sacred trees and from these the people carved a great book of solid oak. Then as each autumn came, the druids and wise men who dwelt near the Oaks would collect the fallen leaves and would record on them the events of that past year. These where then placed into the Great Book and thus came into being the much fabled and long since lost Chronicles of the Clann Abhainn Cluaidh, from whence this tale is said to come.

# THE GREEN OAK TREE

(Author Unknown)

I'll sing a song about a toon that stands upon the Clyde,

and every time I hear its name my heart is filled with pride.

My mother often told me as she soothed me on her knee,

that Greenock took its name from the Green Oak Tree.

So here's tae the Green Oak that stood upon the square,

and here's tae its roots that still lie slumbering there,

and here's tae my toonsmen wherever they may be,

for I'm proud to say that I'm a branch of the Green Oak Tree.

Now Greenock's no a bonny toon I've heard some folks complain,

for every time they go doon there, there's nothing to see but rain,

but let them say whate'er they may, with them I'll no agree,

for Greenock toon and Greenock folks will aye be dear tae me.

# Grian Chnox

### Early History

The history of the peoples of this area stretches back as far as the first men to walk the earth, the first inhabitants settling here sometime between the fourth and sixth millennia BC. Since this time, the fertile lowlands and sheltered valleys surrounding the district have been continually settled. A great many archaeological remains are to be found throughout the area, dating from the Neolithic era to the seventeenth century.

After the retreat of the ice sheets of the Palaeolithic period (600,000 BC - 22,000 BC), dense woodland began to cover the countryside. Woodlands spread across much of the area which forms Inverclyde today. The earliest evidence of human occupation occurred when Mesolithic people travelled northwards from England to the West of Scotland.

As time moved on, these settlers gained knowledge of simple farming, and they began to make more sophisticated weapons and tools. The remains of Neolithic farmsteads can still be found throughout the region, and distinctive 'cup and ring' markings on stones can be found still in such places as Gourock Golf Course and Lurg Moor.

### Celtic Myths

These ancient people left their mark throughout much of the landscape, and many of the area's prominent place names are of Gaelic origin, such as Auchmead, Knocksnair, Drumfrochar, Finnart, Garvel, Spango and Strone. Others were more recently turned to English, during the early Ordance Surveys, when English map makers found anglified terms more easy to deal with; Ravenscraig, for example, was originally known as Creagnamfiach.

However, often the ancients would also give more personalised titles to the land around which they lived, associating them with particular Gods or Goddesses. The Clyde itself is the greatest example of this. The Celtic people linked the river with the Clutha, or Clotta, the Goddess of the Clyde. In England she was called Clud and Cludoita, and in Wales, Clwyd and the waters in which she ruled were believed to be especially useful in healing. In mythology she is often portrayed as a serpent and is said to have borne a son named Gwawl Fab Clud who appears in several Irish myths. The Goddess Clutha has

*Lady of the Lake*

also been identified as an early version of several characters from the Arthurian Legends, such as the Lady of the Lake and the Lady of Shallott and it has even been suggested that the Kempock stone was once used as a sacrificial site to this now forgotten Goddess.

Lorne is another personification of the land in which the ancient people lived. A tree spirit, he appears as a local derivation of Cernunnos. This God was portrayed sitting in a lotus position with horns or antlers on his head, long curling hair, a beard and sometimes holding a bow or spear. A spirit of the forest, he is closely linked with the wild creatures such as the wolf and the stag, important animals in celtic mythology. In essence this God represented nature, woodlands, reincarnation and rebirth and many localised versions of such a character are found throughout Europe, such as the Green man, Herne the Hunter or the Greek deity Pan. These Gods symbolise the importance with which the ancient people regarded their surroundings, giving life to the names with which they christened their landscape.

## THE SUN AND THE OAK

The origin of Greenock's name has long been the subject of much debate. In

*The Sun God*

the year 1769, one writer said "I came to a flourishing seaport town (Greenock), which takes its name from the monarch of the woods, joined to the colour of nature's carpet." He was, of course, referring to the popular belief that the town takes its name from a green oak which used to grow down by the Clyde. The Oak was considered to be the king of the trees and guardian of the realms held sacred by the Celtic Druids who venerated the Oak and would ceremoniously cut the mistletoe from its branches with a golden sickle. The tree of learning, Druids (duir - doorway) would tutor the young underneath its branches and celtic mythology is littered with tales about these mighty oaks. Certainly the later inhabitants of Greenock believed that the town took its name from such a tree, as the ancient coat of arms showed three mighty oaks, and even today the words of the folk song "The Green Oak Tree" are still remembered.

However, the name Greenock, or Grian Chnox, seems to have been a

*The traditional "Man of the Woods"*

descriptive term used by early inhabitants to refer to some particular hill in the area, Grian being the Gaelic word for 'sun,' and Chnox meaning 'hill' or 'knoll.' Grian was the most widely used Celtic word for the sun, although its roots could also be found in the Greek language (Granaois) and also the Roman (Grannos). The particular hill in question is thought to have been sited above Cathcart street, where the Well Park now stands. Early historians of the time claim that this hill was never found to have been in the shade at any hour of the day. If this is the case, it is entirely plausible that there may have been another etymological explanation behind the town's name.

Just as it was also the ancient word for sun, Grannu or Grannos was also an early continental God associated with the sun God Baal. Shrines to Grannu have been found in Auvergne, France, and in sites all over Scotland, including Perthshire and Edinburgh. On the continent he was regarded as a minor sun God, and God of the healing arts. Like many people today, the early Celts sought out mineral springs for their healing benefits, particularly for degenerative muscle ailments or arthritis. Grannu is also given a role as a harvest deity in a children's rhyme sung at harvest festivals which calls Grannu friend, father, mother, and child. At such festivals, fires would be lit, known as Grannos Torches, which would be carried in processions. This tradition is said to have been maintained in parts of the highlands until the early eighteenth century.

If the hill after which Greenock is named was never found in the shade at any time of the day, it is entirely possible that the ancient people who first lived in this area used the site as a place of worship to this ancient God. Certainly the area around the Well Park was the oldest part of the town, and though we have records of a castle situated there as early as the thirteenth century, it is possible that there may have been a settlement there which predated this, building on an established tradition which goes all the way back to some of our early ancestors.

Whatever the truth, one does not have to struggle to spot the irony in the name Sunny Knoll being attached to one of the wettest places in the country; yet you need only to witness the sun rise on the other side of the river on a summer morning to understand why the ancients christened the site as they did.

*Lorne of The Trees Woodcut*
*Designed by Ross Ahlfeld & Carved by Eddie O'Donnell*

Wolf and Eadwacer

The men of my tribe would treat him as game:
If he comes to the path they will kill him outright.

Our fate is forked.

Wolf is on one island, I on another.
Mine is a fastness: the fens girdle it
And it is defended by the fiercest men.
If he comes to the camp they will kill him for sure.

Our fate is forked.

It was rainy weather, and I wept by the hearth,
Thinking of my Wolf's far wanderings;
One of the captains caught me in his arms.
It gladdened me then; but it grieved me too.

Wolf, my Wolf, it was wanting you
That made me sick, your seldom coming,
The hollowness at heart; not the hunger I spoke of.

Do you hear Eadwacer? Our whelp
Wolf shall take to the wood.
What was never bound is broken easily,
Our song together.

# SUN AND THE HUNTER

In the days before man constructed ideas from his own importance,
the sun shines down on an oaken grove, and an ancient religion flourishes...

now

I emerge from the grove of oaks, carrying fresh meat; a necessary kill which will ensure my family sees another dawn. The white will soon be on the green, and the smaller animals are making nests for themselves, showing sense and hiding their head away until the sun bids them welcome out onto the verdant hills once more in the six-month.

I look out, as I so often do, over the hills at this place where my kind have settled. At times it seems as good as any other; at times, I wonder if it is not something more. Even that word - settled - rings strangely as it runs through my thoughts; as if any creature ever *settles*.
Something makes me turn my head sharply downwind; my mate, my chosen, stands stiff and somehow sad at the bottom of the hill, not speaking, not calling out to me, simply waiting for me to return to her, to bring her what offerings the land has seen fit for me to obtain, to keep the balance. Her eyes are anxious, somehow, though they still flash, as they somehow ever will, with the fire I recognized the first time I saw her, head bent to drink at a lake on a morning when the air was still and warm on my skin. The chill is beginning to set in my body, and I muse without bitterness that if I could make a pleasant face for her, then I would. Instead I lope awkwardly down the rocky hill, toward the mother of my children, carrying some other poor creature's dead child with me. Such is the way.

ago

None of my fellows, none of the oldest among us even, knows when we came to these lands; guesses are made, to be sure, that we came down out of the North lands many years ago, or perhaps from over the water by some means we can only wonder about. Nevertheless, my father's father, or some father before him, played his part in choosing these lands for us, and we have been happy here. We respect this land; this sky; these seasons which pass so quickly and seem to have a purpose. To do otherwise would be foolish. We must know *what* we are; this seemed more important to me then, in those early times, when nothing was sure, than the questions of *where* and *why*.

now

We eat, all together now, silent in respect for the food hunted and gathered before us, I am cruelly reminded of the one thing which may yet defeat us from within; power. Power, and the lust for power. A tribe seems to gather

around whatever source of strength they see, and those who will not gather see fit to take control for themselves.

One such individual rises before the rest have finished eating, slowly making his way around the perimeter of those who are still noisily feeding. His eyes never leave me, his intentions all too clear without words. My mate casts nervous eyes toward me, but all my concentration is on the pretender to the throne I did not ask for, but will not give up without a fight.

I stand, back erect, my eyes locked with the dark-haired one whose name I know but vaguely; as our eyes lock I know him. He is one of many, self-important, needing to show himself as strong but unwilling to prove himself. It is no challenge to be the better in this contest of wills.
A low noise begins in my throat; the threat of violence, no more. My feet do not move, my head still, my gaze not lowering once, my eyes never flicking to my family, to the rest of my kind for guidance, never once leaving his.

He seems to have some strength, I'll give him that, does Black-hair; he keeps my gaze for a good few long moments, before dropping his gaze to the ground for a brief time. He raises his head once more, eyes still full of an indolent hatred, but this battle is over; he knows it, too. Presently, he steps back, turning away from me for the first time since this small power-struggle began, and takes his place.

A short time later, the incident is forgotten. A good meal is more important, after all.

ago
These past times have seen great changes for us; once we thought ourselves the only tribe in these coastal lands, but more come every twelve-month, it seems. Tribes the like of which I have never set eyes on before. Tribes who mean us harm; tribes who seem to fear us as if we were monsters. Still among all this, boundary-setting and fighting and home-building and hunting and starving in the lean times, I must be strong. It seems as if I carry all of them on my shoulders at times.

My family. Keep my family safe. These are the thoughts which keep my head high. These are the words which run through my head as I rest in whichever temporary shelter we have found for this night.
Keep my family safe.

now
The white fades from the ground, and quickly; it is dark, and then it is light, and then the green returns. The very air feels different in my nose; sharper. There is happiness all around us. The young ones play around their parents' feet, unmindful of how close they came to death, and unmindful of the possibility of it ever happening again. Many times I envy them their innocence. Soon we must all teach them to fear, like we fear. A hateful task.

Life, if such a word can be attributed to our tribe, returns to normal by and by. We hunt, we eat, we find shelter. We are careful to keep from those who may hurt us; careful to let intruders know we mean them harm. Such is the way.

ago
When first I bested One-eye and took on a mantle of power I do not yet fully understand, I was full of good intentions. I would be a great leader; I would defend the weak and use the strong to make us all stronger; I would feed each and every mouth, slake every thirst and lead my fellows to a home without fear or cold.

Such lofty ideals were driven from me by the Wise One. The oldest among us, there was a wordless agreement that each of the hunters would share his kills with the Wise One, long since too old to hunt for himself. Such kindnesses within our tribe surprise me still. Once, the grey old creature came to me as I sat aside from the others, my insides churning with new responsibilities, and spoke to me long and low.

He told me all the things which were in my mind; told me how foolish they were. He read my mind; aye, and broke it, too. He had seen a great many things, and he spoke only sense. Only now can I be grateful to him.

He was the first to tell me that the earth and the water and the sun were not my friends; they did not help me out of choice. They were as gods, and must be worshipped and respected as such. Only by entering into such an agreement with these elements could I ever hope to use them to see my kind settled and at peace.

Only now do I understand him, with this hateful cold six-month behind us and the sun once again home in the above, where he belongs.

now
Another meal; another hearty feast, and I give silent thanks to those who

deserve it. I look out over the hill, down into the valley, where the Two-legs stand in their circle, arms linked and raised, giving thanks in their own way to the sun for their food and shelter. They seem to have captured part of the sun; it glows in their midst, orange and flickering. If I could muster such a power, surely even the Wise One would be proud.
But he is gone long since. Long since.

If I were to walk down this hill now, to move among the Two-legs on my four good legs, what might they think? I know they fear me, and they hope to make me fear them. Things were ever so. Even so, I wonder. Might, perhaps, we find common ground, common gods, common fears? I cannot know. I stay where I am. They stay where they are. Perhaps this is what keeps the balance. Perhaps.

Black-hair is upon me before I know it, leaping onto my back from behind, his teeth snapping at my throat. Doubtless when he spreads tales of this, he will emerge the hero, defending himself from the old one whose mind has gone.

He is young, but not using his full strength; he thinks this old one too feeble to bother with. I shall teach him otherwise. I throw him from my back and pounce, holding his body down with mine and seeking out the tender flesh of his throat. I remember playing with him when he was a pup, but this thought is gone in an instant. Before I can close my jaws on his flesh, he has scratched out at me, blinding me in one eye. I only have a moment to mark an irony before his teeth are in me, tearing and ripping, a deep growl rising from us both, lifted toward the sun.

I cannot tell how long I lie dying; the time is marked only when my mate, my chosen, comes to me, head lowered, whimpering and scratching at the ground with her paws. She buries her snout in my blood-blackened pelt for the last time, and I am reminded that the wolf is a lonely hunter, and never sleeps in peace.
Such is the way.

# THE CELTS

### EARLY INHABITANTS

*Celtic village*

By 1800 BC, much of Inverclyde had been settled by the Beaker people who had arrived from Europe, early Celts migrating northwards in search of arable land. Many traces of their presence remain throughout the moor land which lies to the south of Loch Thom and the upper Gryfe reservoir, and these are visible as the foundations of small round-huts, simple in layout, although some have annexed chambers; near them lie the remains of a few larger huts and cairns. Around 1500 - 700 BC the bronze age began to sweep across Europe, bringing with it the first true Celtic tribes. The first of these new tribes were the Goidels or Gaels, fair-haired, blue-eyed settlers from central Europe who are thought to have responsible for many of Britain's early ancient monuments.

Celtic culture is thought to have developed in Hallstatt in modern day Austria. Here the bronze age settlers controlled great salt mines which made them wealthy and before long the population of the tribes had grown too great to be sustained by the land. Thus the tribes began spreading west and north into France and from there they colonised Ireland and Britain, moving up the west coast to Scotland.

In Inverclyde simple huts and burials in short stone cists have been found in the throughout the district and throughout much of the land now covered by Muirshiel country park. The Celts of this time were organised into tribes, led by chieftains. Women within the tribe were treated with equal respect as men, and there are many reports of women warriors and druids holding places of great importance within the tribe. During the years after 1500 BC, the Celtic tribe native to this area were known as the Damnoii and, despite the popular image the Romans and Greeks had of the 'Keltoi' as barbarians who sacrificed innocents and drank to excess, the gaelic speaking Damnoii were in fact one of the most peaceful and

*Serpent stones*

respectful of the early Celtic tribes.

## THE DAMNOII

Related to the Damnonians of Devon and Cornwall, the Damnoii were late Bronze Age and early Iron Age settlers, a powerful tribe who owed allegiance to the Welsh chiefs of the time. Most were simple farmers, who cultivated the land, hunting when harvests

*The Celtic tribes of Scotland*

were poor. They lived in small villages, and later in larger settlements which could have been called townships. There are still remains of a Damnoii hut circle at Lurg moor and there is thought to have been a sizeable Damnoii settlement at Langbank. Here the Celts had built Crannogs - artificial wooden islands with huts constructed on them - as a place of safety during dangerous times. They also constructed boats made of oak, some of which were recovered during excavation of the site in the 1901 by J Bruce. The Damnoii survived several invasions from Pictish settlers, and where still relatively powerful at the time of the Roman Invasion, which they also successfully endured. After the Roman retreat, the Damnoii merged with several other tribes under the early Kingdom of Strathclyde.

## ANCIENT MONUMENTS

Like most Celts, the Damnoii worshipped many God and Goddesses under a highly sophisticated religious system governed by the Druids. There is a great

*The terrifying Wicker Man*

deal of evidence to suggest that many of the religious practices of the Celts revolved around human sacrifice, and the Romans claim that the Druids sacrificed criminals or tribal outcasts in wicker baskets, an early form of the Wicker Man burning ceremonies which developed in the third century A.D.

Evidence of these sacrifices was found during excavations in Skelmorlie. Here the Damnoii worshipped at what is widely regarded as one of the most remarkable, yet understated antiquities in Scotland - Serpent Mound. This mound, perhaps artificially constructed, is situated two miles south of the village, where the Meigle burn flows into the river. Snoddy, in his book "Round About Greenock" gives an insightful description of the site;

*"In a casual look round one discovers a well-defined mound, which rises perhaps sixty feet above sea-level, and is forty feet high from its own base; this mound dies into a flattened ridge, which as it recedes, swings round to the left, and for thirty yards or so merges into the background: it then reappears, curving forward and inward, and is completed opposite the point at which it began. From the bank in the rear to the tail it rises into three or four lesser mounds, which decrease in size as you pass outwards. There is therefore a by no means exact, but from a natural viewpoint a rather remarkable mound ridge, which with a lessening body presents a horse-shoe or serpentine form."*

*The Kempock Stone in Gourock*

The first excavations of this curiousity were conducted in 1877 by the archaeologist Dr Phene, after he had discovered a similar mound on the shores of Loch Nell near Oban. Phene concluded that the mounds were of artificial construction, and had been used by the Damnoii for the purposes of Serpent and Sun worship, just as they are thought to have used the Kempock stone, upon which are carved the images of a serpent and a cat. Phene's excavations at Skelmorlie uncovered an 80 foot long paved platform, the remnants of charred bones from cremation rituals, and several larger stones thought to have formed part of an altar. According to Phene the latitude of the site would place it in direct line with the rising point of the sun on the longest day, and would therefore have been used by the Damnoii during midsummer rituals. Several other scientists and archaeologists visited the site in the years after Phene's discovery, although no firm conclusions were ever reached and instead the Serpent Mound, like the ancient Damnoii, seems to have passed out of history.

## SERPENT MOUND

Blood, stone.
Chalk, bone.

Baals fire ever burns.

Land, sea.
Blood, tree.

Baals fire ever burns.

Hill, ash.
Land, flesh.

Baals fire ever burns.

# LAND OF
# THE STRANGERS

*In the years of Roman occupation, Fingal, the mythical Celtic hero despatches
his warriors into the region south of the Clyde,
the mysterious Land of the Strangers...*

A tale of the times of Old. The deeds of days of other years. Clutha of
many streams, dark wanderer of vales in the Land of Strangers, far from
Selma, I behold your course neath Balclutha's empty halls and in sight of
the mighty Grove of Oaks which stand like broken clouds on a hill, when
we see the sky through their branches, and the moon passing behind.
There once dwelt the noble Carthon, son of Clessamor and kinsman of
the fair haired Fingal.

And as the bards proclaimed, Carthon did not die unknown, and the
children of years to come shall hear of his fame; when they sit around the
burning oak, and the night is spent in songs of old. Long will they sing of
the beauty that was his home, for grand were the halls of his youth and
great were the feasts therein, and all the chiefs of Clutha would gather
there to swear oaths of league and friendship The gates of Balclutha were
never to be found shut, for all were welcome,  and the bards of old would
come hither and sing of great deeds and how things came to be. Oh that
I could hear those sweet songs now. A tale of the times of old. The deeds
of days of other years. But I have seen the walls of Balclutha, and no
longer are her towers mighty and fair, but desolate and broken did I find
them, and the ghosts of many did wander there in sight of the deer. The
voice of the people is heard no more and the stream of Clutha was removed
from its place by the fall of the walls. The thistle shook. The moss whistles
on the wind of far off lands. The fox looked out from the windows, the
grass of the walls waves round his head.  Darkness dwells in Balclutha
and all is silent now.

Into the shadow of this fallen palace did fair haired Fingal, King of shields
send three bards of great fame. Often did we pass over the sea to the land
of the strangers, our swords returned not unstained with blood, and many
a secret stream, or hidden forest had played host to the heroes of Fingal.
Beneath one such place did we rest our boat, Fillian of the plains of Morven,
Gaul of the dark hills and Ossian, young in the fields, the son of Fingal,
who does sing to you now. Watched by none but the trees themselves.
Three shields did we bear before us as we marched into the realm of
Calderannon, Chief of Clutha  he that had slain the brothers of Gaul. To
raise a stone in memory of past deeds and heroes fallen was our task, lest
Carthon, who like the great Oak was cut down before his time, never
finds peace in his tomb in the far off land of Morven and the might of

Balclutha be forgotten. But all was not well in the land or the Strangers and as we passed along the road of the enemy through the great valley a sense sorrow and sadness befell us and the ghosts of many a troubled stranger did roam there. Gaul drew forth the sword of his father:

"Listen friends" said the hero "The rule of Calderannon is so harsh that it has awoken the dead. Hear how they cry out for justice. Have I not waited long enough to avenge the memory of my brothers. Oh that Fingal himself were here and we would ride against him, with the wind of a thousand storms at our back."

But such was not our task, and the hour was yet to be appointed when the fair King would send the mighty armies of Morven against Calderannon and Gaul the son of Morni would have his revenge. "Come friends." said Fillian "The night is gathering around. Here let us pass the hours of darkness, by these cold waters that wind towards the domain of Clutha."

Strange dreams befell the heroes of Morven that night, and the ghosts of the dead did after not too long a time bid me to awake quick and to make ready for attack.

"Arise, Gaul of the dark hills, for the time of your vengeance may now be at hand and not Ossian alone shall meet the foe."

"The ghosts of the unrestful did wake me before your cries my friend." Replied the son of Morni. "But victory may elude us this day. A great host do we face now."

"Did thou think to go to battle without the fair son of Clatho? Hark friends, Fillian awakes and his sword sings of war."

And the three heroes looked through the morning dawn at the great force bearing down on them on the hills above, dark like the night since departed and the storm clouds gathering above. The men of Calderannon had come, their harsh lord marching at the head of their host, like the stag of the herd. But as they rode like the wind towards the three, a great noise blew forth from some unseen horn. And an even greater host poured forth to meet the mighty men of Calderannon. Who comes to the land of the strangers with his greatest around him? The sunbeam pours its bright stream before him, cracking the dark clouds and thunder cried forth. Onwards he came, down from the high hills striding from wind to wind and  folding himself in the wing of the storm. And as if called forth by some dream to aid his greatest soldiers, Fingal the fair haired, son of Comhal and King of Morven had come. Again the eagle-wing of his helmet sounded like the war horns of old. The rustling blasts of the west, unequal, rush through early morn.  The sound spreads wide and far on long lost winds that echo no more. The heroes rise, like the breaking of a proud rolling wave against ancient walls unseen. They stand on the heath, like

oaks with all their branches round them, when they echo to the stream of frost, and their withered leaves are blowing to the wind. And such a host the men of Calderannon had never beheld, and so many fled that they surely thought the ghosts of the dead themselves had arisen and asked vengeance for the Land of the Strangers. The battle was swift and the victory belonged to Finagl and the heroes of Selma..

Two green hills surround a narrow plain. The blue course of a stream, claimed in victory by Fingal, finds its home there. Here on its banks rested the warriors of Morven, rejoicing at the arrival of their mighty King. The valleys are quiet and sad around, and success in battle lightens little the fear of attack. Fingal, at length, resumed his soul and imparted the tale of his arrival at such a fortunate hour.

"Hail to you my brave sons. A dream and the vision of Cathlin of Clutha did warn me of trouble in the Land of Strangers and bid me to come to thy aid. I heard her half formed words and dimly beheld the shape of things to come. Fate has written it, and now the time has arrived for more than a stone to be raised. The ghosts of heroes slain walk unavenged, and injustice reigns in this land. Battle is before us and Calderannon and the watchers of the Walls shall feel the cold steel of our blades."

Such words brought fire to the hearts of Fingals men, and songs of war filled the ghostly valley as harp and sword were raised.

And then from the Grain Chnox came a bard, sent by Corlic the meikle, hero of the Strangers and friend of Fingal, King of shields, bidding the heroes of Morven to come feast with him neath the sacred Oaks. Weary were the warriors and in need of rest, thus they accepted the offer with open hearts and open hands. A green knoll, in the bosom of greater hills, sits peacefully above the winding stream of Clutha. Song whistles on the air, which tastes sweet to the mouth and the roe runs wild and free amongst fern and thistle. Overhead the sun watches over like father to his children, until night comes and the dark robed moon extends her hand and all the heavens are set alight with fire of a thousand stars. Here on this hill, midst the sacred Oaks, who like the warriors of Morven, stand tall and proud, dwelt the wise and the true in the shadow of the kings of old now long forgotten. And here too, dwelt Corlic the meikle, Chieftain of the Oaks and friend of Fingals heroes. Meikle he may be, but proud he stood, like the tower under siege, his eyes like flames of fire that burn with the power of the tree he does so love.

"Hail to thee Fingal, King of Morven. A welcomed sight thou truly is in the trouble land of the Strangers. Long have the days been since the green

Oaks of Grannu played host to such a mighty and just band of heroes, and never have such arrived at a time when they were more needed. But come now, let us not talk of such things."
And Fingal looked on the fair haired stranger:
"Let it be so. Our journey has been a long and tiring one, and the heroes of Selma have a need to lighten their hearts, and let sleep all talk of battle."
Corlic kindled the oak of feasts, and all thought of war was laid aside. Then a great meal was prepared and all set to eating, and no man's desire went without an equal share in the feast. The bards of long memory came forth, with harps and soft voices. And great songs were heard that night, of the seeding of the sacred Oaks and how things came to be as they are in the land of the strangers. And the flame of the oak arose, and the tales of heroes were told. By the light of a hundred torches they danced and made merry, and the hearts of all were made light and happy.

But as they laid to the rest , dreams descended on the heroes neath those sacred Oaks, and many a vision was had that night. Yet none was found greater than Fingal's himself, who once more met with the spirit of a stranger. Fingal awoke from this dream, in which the hero had faced once more the mournful form of Cathlin Of Clutha, who many moons before had sought refuge in the fair halls of Selma where Fingal is King. She came from the way of the ocean. Her face was pale, like the mist of Cromla. Dark like the hills were the tears of her cheek. Often was a dim hand raised from her robe which was ever changing like the clouds of the desert. "Why weeps the fairest daughter of the strangers?" said Fingal with a sigh; "why is thy face so pale, pretty wanderer of the heavens?" But silence prevailed and she left him in the midst of the night. But Fingal knew she mourned the sons of her people, that were to fall by the hand of Calderannon. But more so, she mourned for the forgotten glory of Balclutha.

And then the hero awoke from rest. Still he beheld her and the proud towers of Balclutha in his soul. The sound of Gaul's steps approached. The king saw the sword of his father at his side: for the faint beam of the morning came over the waters of Clutha, bringing dim light to the grove. "What do the foes in their fear?" said the rising king of Morven: "or fly they through the valley of the dead, or wait they the battle of our steel? But why should Fingal ask? I hear their voice on the early wind! Awake friends, and make ready for war!"

So it was that the heroes of Morven and Grain Chnox did gather together as one mighty host, and Corlic did swear his oath to Fingal. And all did

follow the fair haired son of Comhal, for no sword shone brighter than his, no sing more clearly of victory. And with the blessing of the wise they did go, Fingal and his heroes, onwards to Lurg heath and the den of Caesar's standard bearers, the allies of Calderannon.

On a hill in sight of the fort did they make ready for battle, as the sun rose high in the sky. And like a wolf from the den, Calderannon came forth with his host, and the two armies faced each other across the heather. Well matched they were, sword for sword, man for man.
And their on the heath the warriors stood their ground, and the clamour of battle rose on both sides. Then it began. Arrows leapt from the string, spears flew from the hand, and the cries of war were heard all around.

Gaul rushed on, like a whirlwind in Ardven. The destruction of heroes is on his father's sword. Through the ranks he cut, like a meteor burning the night sky, searching for he who sent his brothers to the tomb. But Calderannon was like the fire of the desert in the echoing heath of Lurg. My own sword rose high, and flamed in the strife of blood. We pursued and slew, down through the hills towards the banks of the mighty river. As stones that bound from rock to rock; as axes in echoing woods; as thunder rolls from hill to hill, in dismal broken peals; so blow succeeded to blow, hand to hand, strength to strength, death to death, as Fingal's heroes swept onward.

But still Calderannon closed round Morni's son, as the strength of ten tides when a storm does master them. Corlic half rose from his hill at the sight. "Go my aged bards," began the Chief of the Oaks. "Remind the mighty Gaul of war. Remind him of his fathers. Give weight to the yielding fight with song, song that enlivens war." And thus the harps began, raising high their tune above the noise of battle. And words as mighty as swords began:
"Whirl round thy sword as a meteor at night: lift thy shield like the flame of death". And with this the hero's heart beat high. But Calderannon came with battle and with the power of a hurricane, he cleft the shield of Gaul in twain. The heroes of Morven and Grain Chnox fled.

And to the long bank did we come, where the fishers with boats of oak, dwell in the shadow of Balclutha. Night came quickly that day, and the heroes set watch around the fishers homes, the fear of attack on their minds. So it was that they passed that night in sight of the walls, burning no fire lest they be seen, and looking sadly on Balclutha which lay far on

the other bank. And as morning broke, they held council, and fair haired Fingal made ready once more for battle:

"Chieftain of the Oaks! Thou rock that weathers the storm! Whilst thou lead my battle, for the Land of the Strangers? No weak branch is thy spear, no fallen leaf thy shield. Behold heroes of Selma. He is strong as a thousand streams and worthy of great songs. Raise the voice, O bards and bring forth the ghosts of Balclutha, that they may aid us in battle."

"Arise," said the Corlic, "Fingal arise. For I see the ships of the enemy, born on the waves of Clutha herself. Many, King of Morven, are the foe. Many the warriors from behind the walls, that march in the name of an unseen Emperor from a far off land.."

"Corlic" replied Fillian, "thy fears have increased the foe. Look, for Calderannon comes by way of land, tall as blackened stone, and darker still. Onward he marches, and on the beach we must face him."

And the cries of war were let loose, the horns sounded, the harps struck. To the east and west the heroes fought, and like the wolf cornered, they where ever the more fearsome. Now I behold the chiefs, in the pride of their former deeds. Their souls are kindled at the battles of old; and the songs of the bards and the actions of other times. Lightning pours from their sides of steel. Back to back they fight, with the strength of a hundred men, toppling all in their path. Bright are the chiefs of battle, Fingal and Corlic, in the armour of their fathers. Gloomy and dark, their heroes follow like the gathering of storm clouds behind the red meteors of heaven.

As the rising of storm winds, or the lonely roars of troubled seas, when some dark ghost cries through the mists. So haunting is the sound of the host, swift-moving over the field. Gaul is tall before them. The bards raise the song by his side, where surely the ghosts of his brothers walk. He strikes his shield between, and makes ready for battle. And then Calderannon came, the slayer of heroes poised to kill again.

And there midst the rolling waves of battle, man fought man, shield met shield; steel struck steel. Darts hiss through air; spears ring on mails; and swords on broken buckles sound. As the noise of an aged grove beneath the roaring wind, when a thousand ghosts break the trees by night, such was the roar of arms. Mighty indeed were the two warriors, but in the end Calderannon did fall beneath the sword of Morni and the watchers of the wall fled.

Thus the heroes of Morven were victorious, and the land of the strangers

freed from harsh rule, the ghosts of its sons avenged and put to rest in their tombs. And Fingal looked on the meikle chieftain of the Oaks, who stood before him only as tall as a child, but whose eyes burned with bravery worthy of song.

"Corlic the meikle you may be, but as mighty as a mountain thou most surely is, and in deeds, taller still."

I saw the heartened soul of the stranger, and did foresee that this mighty hero, worthy of a place in Morven, would bring peace to the land.

And so things were when Fingal and his heroes took leave of the Land of the Strangers, leaving in their wake a mighty stone. Long may it stand there, in sight of the once fair towers of Balclutha, a memory to the deeds of days past and heroes long in the tomb. And on stormy nights it shall give shelter to those that have none, and watch over the traveller who sleeps beneath it. The songs of old shall sound in his dreams and years that are long forgotten shall return. The mighty heroes of times gone shall rise before him and the fires of a thousand oaks will burn on the wind. And then in the mists of the flames shall he see the mighty king of Balclutha, who fought with the strength of a thousand streams. And when morning comes and he awakes from such dreams, he shall ask about the stone, and the aged and grey shall reply:

"This is Fingal's Stone, which was raised in memory of the great halls of Balclutha and all who did dwell therein."

But alas not always shall the stone be in sight of Balclutha, for in my dreams I foresee a time when it shall be toppled and the feast that is the deeds of old shall once again fall from the table of remembrance.

A Forgotten Song of Ossian

# FINGAL

*A Roman Legionnaire*

"He was an experienced traveller, a wise king, a skilful general, a patriotic soldier, a generous man and an accomplished physician."

Waddell

### THE ROMAN INVASION

Scotland in the first century AD was little more than a collection of scattered tribes of varied allegiances. While large parts of Europe were falling under the control of the ever-expanding Roman empire, the Scots lived as they always had, farming the land and the sea. However, the Romans realised that if they were ever to hold Britain, the North must be made secure.

Despite having had contact with the tribes of Britain for over a hundred years, it was not until AD 47 that the Romans finally invaded. The 40,000 strong army with its superior training and weaponry was more than a match for the Celtic tribes of southern Britain, and while some, such as Boudicca of the Iceni, mounted resistance, most surrendered themselves to the benefits of Roman rule.

However, resistance in Scotland was a different story, and the tribes here were able to keep the Romans out until the invasions of Agricola in AD 81. After this time the Romans continued to occupy Scotland periodically for the next one hundred years. Between periods of occupation, the Roman forces would retreat behind Hadrians Wall, venturing out for campaigns during the summer months.

In AD 142, the Romans extended their frontier by building the Antonine wall along the Forth-Clyde line, comprising of a series of forts, smaller fortlets and signal posts. The remains of a small well preserved Roman fortlet can still be seen on Lurg Moor above Greenock, and from there a road ran westwards to a signal post near Dunrod Hill, before turning south again to another fortlet north of what is now Outwards Reservoir. From here, the Romans occupied the most North Westerly corner of their Empire, keeping watch over the western flanks of the new frontier.

As a province of the Empire, Britain was subject to a complex system of government. The local fortlets were linked through the chain of command to the Forts at Bishopton and Barrochan, and beyond that to the main Antonine fortress at Castlecary. A network of roads was built by the army to allow legions to move through the territory quickly and suppress frequent uprisings among the locals. Yet not all locals were opposed to the Romans, and often

*THE ANTONINE WALL*

those chiefs who co-operated with them were rewarded, and the children given a Roman education.

## FINGAL
"In reviewing a character and leader like this, one is increasingly reminded of Charlemagne."   Waddell

At this time the tribes of Ireland and Scotland were dominated by the legendary warrior Fingal (known as Finn MacCumhail, in Ireland) and his band of mercenary heroes. It was a dark time for the people of Scotland and the mythical hero was said to have waged war on the Roman oppressors. Whatever the true facts of Fingal's character, life and exploits, they have been long since lost amidst a wealth of tales and poems celebrating him as a legend, a true champion who saved the people from a tyrannical empire.

It is difficult to pinpoint the roots of Fingal; stories have passed from hand to mouth down through the ages, from the highlands of Scotland to the rocky coasts of Ireland, all regions that the legendary hero is said to have called home. Some record him as a giant, others as a supernatural warlord, while to others he was simply a good and wise king.

He is remembered throughout all of the Celtic world as a champion who ruled over parts of Both Ireland and Scotland, and while exact dating of his exploits is impossible, it is widely agreed that he opperated some time during the 2nd century A.D.

According to old Irish mythology, Fingal was born the son of Cumal, (hence his name - Finn MacCumal, now shortened to Fingal) a Celtic chieftain, who was killed in battle by rival clan leader Morna. This meant that Fingal would inherit the throne, though as he was still an infant, his mother saw fit to protect him from his enemies by entrusting him to the care of two women. Bodhmall, a female druid, and Liath Luachra, his nurse, raised the young Fingal in secret, preparing him for the day when he would take his place as King.

Fingal had many adventures during this period of training, the most famous of these being his encounter with 'the salmon of knowledge,' a mythical creature which would impart any who caught it with endless wisdom. After catching the fish, Fingal burned his finger on it during its cooking; sticking his finger into his mouth to cool it, he discovered his new prophetic gift. With his new found knowledge, Fingal spent many years traveling far and wide throughout Scotland and Ireland, gathering a great band of warriors from both nations and finally after many trials and exploits, taking him as far afield as Scandanavia, he returned home to claim his throne.

### The Ossian Myths

In all the myths that surround him, Fingal is always followed by a cadre of warriors  known as the Fianna,  a legendary band of heroes who defended Ireland and Scotland and kept law and order. Members included among others, Fingals son Fergus, Gaul, son of Morna and  the warrior Caoilte who was Kings right hand man and who is reputed to have conversed with St. Patrick many centuries later in the 'Dialogue of the Elders', extolling the virtues of the Celts to him. Other notable followers included Oscar, the greatest warrior, Connan, and Diarmait O'Duibhne, who eloped with Fingals betrothed Grania.

Yet the greatest among all these heroes was Fingals son, Ossian, a blind bard whose duty it was to record the deeds of his mighty father. The poems Ossian would write about his father's life would eventually form the cornerstone of the vast mythos passed down about Fingal and his deeds. The traditional Ossianic material, consisting of about 80,000 lines, expresses nostalgia for the heroic pagan past and the ballads seem to have been  preserved both in Ireland and in the highlands of Scotland; 28 of them were included in the 16th-century Scottish anthology The Book of the Dean of Lismore. Of these, the epic poem 'Fingal' is the longest, and is largely concerned with Fingal's conflict with Swaran, a Scandanavian chief who invaded parts of Ireland and Scotland. In the second great poem 'Temora,' an aging Fingal returns to Ireland from Caledonia in order to reclaim his throne from the usurping chief  Cairbar. Other poems deal with the Fianna's adventures further afield, battling

Frontispiece from "The Poems of Ossian" London 1762

*Ossian, the blind bard.*

with the early Vikings, who in Gaelic belief came from the fabulous world of Lothlind (in reality Norway) and were beings of the otherworld. Today Ossian is known primarily through the work of the Scottish poet James Macpherson, who in the 1760s published several volumes purporting to be translations of the blind poets work. The work was an instant success, becoming a cornerstone of the Romantic movement and subsequently revered throughout Europe ; Napoleon carried a copy with him; Brahms and Schubert wrote music to accompany them.

## BALCLUTHA

"I have seen the walls of Balclutha, but they were desolate, the fire had resounded in the halls and the voice of the people is heard no-more. The stream of Clutha was removed from its place by the fall of the walls. The thistle shook. The moss whistles in the wind. The fox looked out from the windows, the grass of the walls waves round his head."

*Ossian; Cathlin Of Clutha*

The poems which deal with the Fianna's exploits in Scotland make frequent mention of a great palace known as Balclutha, the site of which was once the subject of much debate. Numerous locations were sugested, including Rutherglen and Lanark. Today however, most scholars agree that Balclutha is in fact a corruption of Alclyud, the rock of the clyde I.e Dumbarton Rock. Excavations at the site reveals evidence of structures dating as far back as the Bronze age, hardly surprsing when one considers the nature of the location. The site is surrounded on three sides by water with a high summit, making it the perfect location for any fortress.  It also lies on the edge of the Antonine wall and as a result any chiefs in residence there would undoubtedly have had close contact with the Roman invaders. In the Ossian poems we find Fingal and his followers making a number of visits to Balclutha, and to the region south of the Clyde which they knew as the land of the strangers, due to the strange tongue which the inhabitants there spoke. The strangers were Britons living under roman rule, the descendants of the Celtic Damnoii, who at this time owed allegiance to the Welsh Kings. Here the followers of Fingal are said to have done battle with the Romans and their allies from the

*Finnoch Bog in Inverkip.*

south. Indeed, much of the landscape still bare names which remember Fingal. Finnoch bog behind Inverkip for example is corruption of Finn wich seid - Fingals washing place were the hero is likely to have stopped when in pursuit of Romans. In Ossian we find that two of the brothers of the hero Gaul fell in battle against Caldarannan, "a chief of Clutha", who is thought to have taken his name from Caldar water which flows in the hills behind Loch Thom. Thus we find that in Inverclyde, as in many other parts of the Celtic world, echoes of this great and far famed warrior can still be found.

"The whole of the region from the coast of Inverkip to the roman road at Maulsmyre has been the theatre for his forgotten campaigns. Forgotten by all but Ossian in his sorrowful glimpse at Balclutha and the ruined strongholds of the Clyde."

Waddell

## Dramatis Personae of the Ossianic Myths

| | |
|---|---|
| Fingal | King of Morven |
| Ullin | the bard of Fingal |
| Gaul (Goll) - | leader of the clan Morna |
| Ossian - | son of Fingal, the renowned warrior and blind bard |
| Fergus } Ryno } | sons of Fingal, warriors and poets |
| Oscar | son of Ossian, the bravest of the Fingalians, youthful and kindhearted |
| Diarmid | the handsomest, the Adonis of the Fingalian mythology, whose slaughter by a wild boar is one of the best known myths of the Ossianic cycle |
| Caoilte | Fingal's nephew, the swiftest of the Fingalians (like the Greek Hermes - Mercury) |
| Connal | petty chief of Togorma |
| Conan Maol | the fool of the Fingalians |

*The inspirational Fingals cave.*

*Fingal Woodcut*
*Designed by Ross Ahlfeld and carved by Eddie O'Donnell*

# The Serpent and the Saint

*An early pilgrim strikes a bargain with a sea goddess,*
*and learns the true value of his faith...*

In days long forgotten, when magic was abroad and there were tales told after every meal, an old oak grove stood on top of the Grian Chnox. Here above the Clyde was a sacred place, a place where the gods of the land and sea met under the one sun.

It came to pass in these days that a traveller arrived in the village that lay beneath the hill. Blane was his name, and he had travelled a long distance from the city of St Peter, carrying with him a casket of sacred soil. As night fell he knocked on the door of the one home in the village where a candle still burned in the window and was greeted by an elderly woman. "I have travelled many miles and tomorrow I seek passage north across the water where I will end my journey. But for tonight I only seek a place to lay my head and a simple meal of fish."

At this the woman appeared distressed. As Blane attempted to console her she recounted the tragic events that had blighted the village in recent days. The start of the fishing season had seen great catches, enough to feed the villagers three times over. But as the days and weeks passed, the boats returned with more fishermen than fish. This caused great strife for the village but it was to be nothing compared to the hardships which were to come. On the fourth Monday before the turning of the seasons ten men went out and seven returned. On the third Monday seven men went out and five returned. On the second Monday five men went out and three returned. Now on the last Friday before the bright half of the year the three men who went fishing on Monday are yet to return.

Blane then asked the elderly woman why only she kept a candle burning and to this she answered:
"The candle burns for the last fishermen of the village, my husband and my two sons."
At this the candle flickered and blew itself, out plunging the room into darkness. A moment later the door flew open and by the waning light of the moon a hunched figure stumbled inside. It was the youngest son, returned from the river without his father or brother. As he warmed himself by the fire he recounted a tale as harrowing as Blane had ever heard.
"When we set out the wind was at our backs, and we sailed out further than we had before, hoping the waters would be brimming with fish. We dropped our nets and hoped for better fortunes. The

day drew on and the sun dimmed and still our nets were empty. We decided to head back to home, but as we tried to haul our nets back, the ropes were dragged from our hands. The water seethed and writhed, and as our boat overturned, I caught sight of a mammoth fin, before it once again flashed beneath the waves. Freezing and spluttering I looked around for my father and brother, but they too had vanished. The waters gave way once again, and our boat was dashed to splinters as a mighty serpent crashed towards the skies. The sight of this hideous visage bearing down on me was the last thing I saw before a terrible dark sleep came upon me. I awoke shivering on the shore."

It now seemed certain that this terrible creature was the source of the village's most recent woes.

Blane now realised that he had little hope of crossing the river before the turning of the seasons; leaving the family with their grief he set out to consult the village elders for a solution to his plight. In a clearing, by the Grove of Oaks, the elders had assembled around a fire.
"I have travelled from the seat of the Holy See, carrying with me a box of consecrated earth. I seek passage over the waters, that I might bless my own church with this hallowed ground before spring turns to summer. Is there no way to cross?"

The elders explained that the creature destroyed every craft which tried to pass, and they had no solution to the problems of their own village let alone the concerns of a passing traveller. Disheartened and fearing that his quest would never be completed, Blane wandered past the Oak Grove and into the dark of the woods beyond.

As he journeyed on through the valley, he found himself in the forest of Ravenscraig where the trees became thick with flickering shadows. Gradually, Blane became convinced that he was being watched. Ahead, peering through the darkness, he could make out the unmistakable eyes of a wolf. As he made to turn tail and run, the shadowy creature stepped forwards into a shaft of moonlight. It was not a wolf, but a man.
"Do not be afraid Blane, my name is Lorne and these are my woods. I understand you wish to cross the Clyde. These are dangerous waters, Clutha, the great lady of the river, is angry."
"What do you know of the great serpent and the deaths of the fishermen?" asked Blane.

"More than the wise village elders do, that I can assure you," replied the shadowy figure. As the sun rose all around them, he went on to explain the delicate nature of the balance which must exist between the land and the sea, and the old gods which are responsible for them. Blane learned that Grian Chnox had long been considered the meeting point of these elemental forces.

"The villagers of these western lands are good people, but they comprehend little of the great gods. They do not understand that these spirits of the earth and the water are selfish and sometimes cruel. They farm the river to feed their families, but they take too much; they offer nothing in return to Clutha, who thinks it fair to take their husbands and sons in return. Even I cannot say when she will decide she has taken enough, and so something must be done to restore the balance."

Blane listened to Lorne intently, but still could not see what part he had to play. "This is not my village, these are not my people. I feel for their loss, but I am one man, and these people face a monster with the strength of a hundred. My concerns lie elsewhere, and with another god."

Lorne shook his head at this last, and spoke again: "You are mistaken. You carry close to your heart the kind of belief which can enable one man to topple mountains. Only this can redress the balance I speak of, and stop the deaths of innocents."

Loarn explained that the trees which grew on Grian Chnox were both sacred and magical and that, if Blane was determined to cross the waters of the Clyde with his precious cargo, then a boat made from one of these same oaks would ensure safe passage.

"You will cross the river, you will end the suffering of this village, and you will return home safely. I can tell you no more. These are simply things that I know."

So saying, Lorne stepped back into the darkness, and Blane was sure that he heard not two feet padding away, but four.

Left with more questions than answers, Blane nonetheless decided to carry out Lorne's wishes; he chopped down the mightiest oak atop the hill, and fashioned it into a boat. As night fell on the last day before the turn of the seasons, he set sail with the sanctified soil, and with a prayer in his heart, he was full of joy at being closer to home. However, the simple boat was no more than halfway across the body of water when there was a clamour and a churning of the water, and the serpent pulled its vast body into the air over Blaine's modest vessel. As he stood frozen in fear, the great beast suddenly spoke.

"I am Clutha, goddess of this river, and you are a land-dweller who will never learn that there is a price to be paid for nets filled with fish and safe crossings. Too often now, the land takes what it pleases, and never gives in return. Will you too cross without paying, little man, and take without giving?"

Blane knew that his time had come, and thinking back to Lorne's words, he knew what he had to do.

"I carry with me the very earth beneath all our feet, earth which is used to honour my god. It is more precious to me than my life, and I would die to protect it. I will show you what an ignorant land-dweller can do to offer you a sacrifice."

So saying, Blane opened the casket of soil and drew out a handful, scattering it into the water before the vast sea serpent.

"This old god is honoured by this, the sacred land of your new god. The toll is paid; the land has taken and has repaid with its own. The people of this river may come and go as they please."

And so the trials were over; the villagers mourned for their dead and carried on living and Blane returned home to the isle of Bute and built his church atop a green hill surrounded by trees.

In later years, a church was built in Blaine's name in the town which was once the village, and some say, as some will, that Blane himself was buried beneath it. But this is another story for another time.

Perhaps the people of the Clyde valley are wiser for this tale; perhaps some of them now know that the sea will only give so much.

# Saint Blane

### Early Celtic Missionaries

Following the departure of the Romans from Scotland, the Druidic religion which had been suppressed, once again came to the fore, though it was now disjointed and fragmented. The ancient ways still flourished among the common man; however the nobility, who still remained highly influenced by Roman ideals and beliefs considered themselves Christian. It was from these noble families that many of the early Celtic Saints emerged. In time they were to cut their links with Rome and lay the foundation stones for a new church, drawing on elements of both the Celtic and the Christian religions. The transition was made easier by the ancient Celtic myths and legends being woven into Christian parable and churches being established on traditional places of pagan worship. The Isle of Bute, was regarded by many

*A traditional missionary saint.*

as a sacred place, and it was here that the new Church would establish one of its earliest missions.

### St Blane's Journey

In the sixth century, Cattan the Irish saint and his sister Ertha settled in Bute in the area now named for them as Kilchattan Bay. Around 565AD Ertha became pregnant to an unknown man. Cattan was furious at this, so much so that, after the birth of her baby, named Blane, he had mother and child cast onto the sea in an oarless boat. This was the custom of the Celts at the time, a similar story is told of the birth of Saint Mungo.

This harsh judgement was carried out to satisfy the demands of the church at the time; however, Cattan had taken precautions to ensure the safety of his sister and nephew, and the coracle washed up safely in Benthorne in Northern Ireland. Here, Ertha and her child were delivered into the care of Saint Comgall of Bangor and Saint Cainnech (Kenneth). For the next seven years, Blane and his mother lived in Ireland, before returning home to Bute in preparation for the young boy's education.

Blane received a classical education  here; Kingarth in Bute would become one of the three most notable seats of knowledge in Scotland. During this time, he is said to have performed several miracles, convincing his uncle of his grace, prompting Blane to undergo a pilgrimage to Rome. As Whitelock notes,

"It was as safe and easy to go to Rome then as now, the well-paved highway leading from Strathclyde direct to the eternal city."

On his return journey, Blane had numerous adventures. He was carrying with him a basket of soil from Rome, intending to use it to consecrate the location of his future church. He landed at Port Lughduch and walked up Glen Callum at the south end of Bute with the basket of earth, only to have it spill on the ground as he climbed the hill. He met a local woman who was on her way to gather shellfish at the shore, and he asked her to help him collect the spilled soil. She refused, however, and Blane cursed her, saying "May it be high tide whenever you go to the seashore for shellfish."

Blane received a grant of land from the local tribal chief and marked off his monastic enclosure. He was now ready to begin the work he had been trained for.

### BLANE'S MISSIONS

Blane's first two missionary journeys took him all over Scotland, from the southern tip of Strathclyde to the northernmost parts of Dalriada. In 600 AD, he undertook his third mission - his goal to establish a centre of work without the disadvantages of an island, from which to spread the word of his new church.

*The ruins of St. Blane's Chapel on Bute*

*Inside St Blane's Chapel.*

The first church known to have been established by Blane during this mission was in Greenock, upon the site now known, applicably, as Kilblain Street. The nearby George Square marks out the area of the original church cemetery where, over the years, several bones have been unearthed.

Blane was, for the people of Inverclyde, one of the first Christian missionaries they encountered, and the establishment of his church would mark their first involvement with Christian religion. Undoubtedly, Blane spent a great deal of time in the area, setting up the location of the church as well as teaching the local inhabitants of the ways of his God, before moving on, leaving one or two of his acolytes behind to continue his work.

It is interesting to note that the next church to be established in this area was St. Lawrence's, set up by the Catholic Church in the middle ages. This saint has the same feast day as Blane, and in both Greenock and Dunblane (Blane's later centre of worship in Scotland), the Roman church introduced St. Lawrence to counteract the devotion of the people to their earlier saint.

Before his death, about which little is known, St. Blane set up other prominent churches all over the country, Strathblane and Dunblane being among the most famous. His work, however, was vigourously carried on by the followers he left behind; the order of monks who would, in time, become known as the Culdees, and who would be the only group of Christian missionaries in this area for the next five hundred years. The local church itself is thought to have been maintained until the time of the Reformation.

To this date, the area around George Square in Greenock has remained a focal point for many varied faiths; more churches have been built in this small area than in any other part of Inverclyde.

# The Wizard & His King

In the days of King Arthur, the religion of the druids begins to fade
and an old wizard seeks out hope for the future...

*From the Chronicle of Rhydderch Hael, King of Strathclyde*

*The air is filled with the sound of war, the sky with the darkness of an approaching storm. Two vast armies locked in battle, rage across the plain. Swords flash from the sheath, arrows fly from the bow, and faith meets faith. And then out of the darkness and the rain comes, a boy. No, not a boy, a man. And he carries with him a flaming sword, and all who challenge him fall prey to it.*

Autumn had come too quickly, thought the old man as he hiked up tree clad slopes, heading north, the leaves crunching under foot. He would be the last to arrive, but then he always was. It mattered not, he already knew what they had to say. In the distance he caught his first glimpse of the torches marking the edge of the clearing. Who would be there, he wondered. The priests of serpent mound would surely send representatives, as would the wise men of Grian Chnox. Perhaps even the men of Kempock would be present, though they held little sway anymore. There may even be a delegation from the isles. Well, he would find out soon enough.

The clearing opened up before him, a wide enclosure surrounded by a ring of oak trees. In the centre stood a huge boulder, the far famed stone of Judgement. Around the base stood eleven Druids, all dressed in various coloured robes, and on the summit of the stone stood a twelfth individual, a grey beard, shrouded in a purple robe, who addressed the old man as he entered the clearing:

"Welcome Lailoken. We feared you wouldn't come."

"You need not have Bran, I was merely delayed somewhat."

"That is as may be, but it has been many years since you walked among us, and we thought you may not have heard the call."

"Do not worry, the Ravens brought me word."

Bran nodded;

"Then we can begin. As you are all aware, a new challenger for the throne is about to emerge. The stars have foretold it. But we do not where or when..."

"I have seen him." Proclaimed Lailoken. "Hael is his name, and he is still but a boy of thirteen."

"A Welsh King? Here? I think not." Uttered one of the Serpent priests.

"Surely you joke with us Lailoken. The signs foretold of a great warlord who would bring glory to the kingdom, not some boy who is not even old

enough to wield a sword." Retorted another.

"How do you know that this Hael boy is the one?" Asked Bran.

"I have seen him in my visions. And you know that I am seldom troubled by false prophecies." Said Lailoken. "I bring you this news so that you might be better prepared for what is to come. But perhaps it was a waste of my time."

"Perhaps it was Lailoken. These past years in the wilderness have clouded your vision, for this boy is not our King."

"Then I am done with you. Debate all you want, a change is coming, whether you like it or not. And this boy will be King, I promise you."

And with that, Lailoken left the clearing and disappeared into the forest from whence he had come.

Long did he wander in the trees that day; why had he even bothered to come? The concerns of man mattered not to him anymore. He was done with them. That evening he made camp on a small hill on the outskirts of the woods, among the ruins of some forgotten stronghold lost to the ravages of time and overgrown with the vine. But he was not alone, for the wolf had spotted him, and taken word of him to his master. Thus as night fell, the old Druid was little surprised when he who is as ancient as the oak appeared amongst the ruins, shrouded in a robe of leaves, with eyes that burned greener than emeralds. And so Lailoken addressed him who few mortals have seen:

"Welcome Lorne of the trees."

"Merlin, it is good to see you."

"Its  Lailoken now."

"Yes, I've heard. The wild hermit of Caledon."

"Among other things." Replied Lailoken.

"I have come here to take counsel with you Merlin. There is war where once there was peace. My land is wounded, my heart saddened."

The forest Lord's voice was soft as the wind.

"It matters not to me."

"Oh but it does. You were always the greatest among the wise. Why have you forsaken them at this their hour of need?"

"All they ever do is talk. Besides, this boy is not my concern. I will not play master to another puppet king. Not again."

"Perhaps, but you cannot hide forever. You may very well claim the boy is not your concern, but you still choose to try and warn them about him. You can sense it. A great change is coming and the wind is no longer at our backs. And you above all should know the dangers we face."

"What would you have me do?"

"Do what you have always done Merlin. Guide those who are lost."

"The druids do not need guidance."

"I was not talking about the druids."
And with that, Lorne disappeared into the trees, leaving Lailoken alone
with his thoughts once more.


Glaurung,  Prince of the Otadeni had come in sight of the bridge, and
turning slightly he surveyed the great force which defended it, bringing a
great many Knights around him.  The Novantae had a  mighty force by the
crossing, guarding the gate. And beyond on the other side there stood
many foes still to be faced.
"Take heart my friends." Shouted Glaurung. "The Novantae shall not have
victory this day."
Then he turned to the young boy who rode alongside him and smiled;
"Fear not young Rhyderrch, you are safe with me."
But the boy was not so sure. For two months now he had rode with Glaurung
as a standard bearer and this was the greatest force they had faced since
he had left Wales. He wished he had not insisted on joining Glaurung.
What care did he have for this far flung Kingdom? None save that it was
the home of parents he had never known, now long in the grave.
 Then the clarion sounded and the mighty army took up position, their
Prince making ready to lead the charge on a proud steed as white as
snow. So the great force poured off the hillside and the two armies met
like the clash of thunder, steel on steel, blade on blade.
Long did they fight that day, with neither side being the clear victor. But
then as the sun waned, the men of the Otadeni, though more skilled,
were far outnumbered. The bridge was not to be theirs. Onward came the
Novantae, and endless stream crossing from the opposite bank, slaying
their foes by the dozen, loosing death across the field.
And there stood Rhyderrch in the midst of the carnage.  Blinded by dust
and smoke and shaking with fear, the young boy ran. And he kept running
until he had left the field far behind. When he finally had the courage to
stop, he found himself in a deep glade, through which ran a fresh clear
stream.  There he rested along while, tending the few scratches he had
received during his flight and contemplating his fate. What would he do
now? He could go back, and even if he did, what would he find? The
Otadeni had surely lost the battle. He would be forced into slavery once
the Novantae discovered him. And if by some miracle Glaurung had gained
victory, Rhyderrch would be killed for abandoning the standard and fleeing
the field. A great chill came over the boy, warmed little by the fire he had
started.
Soon night came upon the little gully, and even the Ravens took flight at
the darkness that seeped into the valley. But while all else living fled for
warmer ground, save poor Ryhderrch, there was something which remained

there. And then out of the shadows it came; a man, with a robe which shone like silver.

And in voice as clear as the sky on a summer day, he spoke to the young boy:

"May I warm myself by your fire."

Rhyderrch nodded, partly out of fear and partly out of joy at the prospect of some company.

"Allow me to introduce myself. I am Lailoken of Caledon."

Still Rhyderrch remained silent, mesmerised by the sight of this strange man. Again Lailoken addressed him;

"And you young boy, have you a name?"

Finally he answered;

"Rhyderrch sir. Rhyderrch Hael, son of Morken."

"And what brings you to such a remote place young master Hael?" Asked Lailoken.

And so Rhyderrch recounted to him the tale of his flight from the field. He told how he had journeyed to this godforsaken land with his ageing uncle, a Welsh chief allied to the Otadeni. Rhyderrch had insisted on accompanying him, so that he might learn more of his parents homeland. But he had found himself all but alone when his uncle passed away some six months ago.

"And since then I have been standard bearer for Prince Glaurung."

Lailoken nodded sagely as the young boy concluded his tale.

"Yes war has dragged a dark cloud across the sky of this land, bringing suffering to all those who reside here. It is sad is it not?"

Rhyderrch nodded.

"And tell me young master Hael, what do you make of all this fighting?"

The young boy seemed puzzled by this question and found further distraction in the mouth watering smells coming from the fire where a large chicken was now roasting on a spit above the flames.

"I don't know sir?"

Lailoken tutted.

"Well surely you must have an opinion. Are you of the contention that the tribes should remain independent entities in their own right, with no interference from the Druids. Or are you of the school which calls for a wholly integrated tribal system over seen by the Magi?"

Rhyderrch stared blankly at the old man and could only wonder were the goblet of mead he was now holding had come from.

"I'm not too sure sir, I mean..." He stuttered.

"Oh for goodness sake boy. If we are going to get anywhere, you really must start forming opinions. Now listen to me." Lailoken raised to his feet and took up position on a large rock before continuing. "This land is ravaged

by war. The tribes who were once united by Roman rule have now began to war with one another, causing great divisions among the Druids, not to mention angering the Gods.  The solution to all this is obvious. The land needs a leader, a King. Am I right young master Hael?"

Rhyderrch was too busy with the bowl of apples which had mysteriously appeared next to him.

"Am I right young master Hael?" Said Lailoken, his voice now echoing through the gully.

Once more the boy nodded. Lailoken continued;

"But it is not that simple. Each of the tribes claims the right to Kingship. And then there is the whole Welsh question to deal with...."

"But what does all this have to do with me?" Asked Rhyderrch.

And Lailoken turned to him and smiled.

"Why young master Hael, you are to be King."


*The air is filled with the sound of war, the sky with the darkness of an approaching storm. Two vast armies locked in battle, rage across the plain. Swords flash from the sheath, arrows fly from the bow, and faith meets faith. And then out of the darkness and the rain comes, a boy. No, not a boy, a man. And he carries with him a flaming sword, and all who challenge him fall prey to it.*

# RHYDDERCH HAEL

*The Battle of Arderryd*

### THE KINGDOM OF STRATHCLYDE

At the beginning of the fifth century AD., the Roman Empire found itself fighting a war on several fronts and had no choice but to withdraw the protection of her legions from Britain in a desperate measure to fight Eastern invaders on the continent. On their departure, the Romans declared Britain an independent and self-governing state, effectively renouncing all claim on the country and thus plunging it into a state of civil war between the different tribes, all of whom battled for control.

Without any single authority to organise a united defence, the Britons were vulnerable to attack from invading barbarians, and over the next one hundred and fifty years, found themselves pushed further northwards by the Saxon and Anglican tribes. At this time, many Chieftains and Kings emerged as heroes against these invaders, though few could rival the successes of Rhydderch Hael, the Ruler of the Kingdom of Strathclyde. Much of the information we have for this King comes from the medieval chronicler Geoffrey of Monmouth. According to him Rhydderch Hael, or Roderic the Generous, was of Roman descent, although he had strong allegiances with the Welsh Kings, and like most other people in Strathclyde at that time he spoke the Welsh language. After uniting the Celtic tribes of the Damnoii, Votadini, Selgovae and Novantae, King Rhydderch seems to have come to the throne of Strathclyde sometime

*Dumbarton Rock*

around 550, while he was still a relatively young boy, possibly no older than sixteen. Like the other Roman Britons, he retained a strong devotion to the Christian religion introduce by his Imperial predecessors. However, the Saxon tribes and the Britons in the south, under the leadership of Gwenddolau were still strong followers of the Druid religion, and even in Strathclyde, there still existed strong support for the pagan teachings. Eventually these dissentions broke into open battle, with the Christian forces of Rhydderch Hael meeting the pagan warriors of Gwenddolau at Arderryd, some eight miles north of Carlisle. Here the King of Strathclyde's forces overran the invaders and today the battle is widely regarded as the decisive victory of Christianity over paganism, a marking point in British history. The following years of Rhydderch's rule saw him establish peace and prosperity throughout his Kingdom, the centre of which was regarded as Dumbarton Rock, where he is thought to have held court. Unlike most Kings of the time, he is said to have died peacefully in his bed, having reached a considerable age.

*Merlin / Lailoken*

### ARTHURIAN LEGENDS

As well as Geoffrey of Monmouth's account of Rhydderch Hael, we also have several stories and myths regarding him which were set down by the Welsh bards. Many of these tales formed the basis of the medieval Arthurian legends, and Rhydderch is regarded as one of the historical figures upon which the mythical King may have been based. Thus we find many similarities between the two Kings. For example, Excalibur is also thought to be very similar to the sword of Rhydderch named 'Dyrnwyn' as spoken of in the ancient Welsh Triads and the Mabinogion. This was known to be one of the 'Thirteen Treasures of Britain.' This sword was revered for being of the Otherworld, and for being able to completely burst into flames, but it was said that it could only be used by someone of noble birth. In early Arthurian legend it was said that thirteen treasures existed in the Otherworld, and these were reputed to have been retrieved from Annwn by Arthur. These were collectively known as the Thirteen Treasures of Britain and the story of their recovery is recounted in the poems of Taliesin. In Welsh tradition, Rhydderch is also thought to have been the husband of Ganieda, the sister of Merlin, and Merlin himself is said to have been at the court of Rhydderch Hael, where he was known as Lailoken or Merlin the Wild man of Caledon. Described usually as lean and tall in stature, with a long white beard, the symbolic essence of Merlin's role in Arthurian legend as the archetypal magician/wizard/counsellor, who employs arcane knowledge and mystical powers for the victory of good over evil, is one of the most enduring in mythology . According to Celtic legend he was a Scottish madman with prophetic abilities, and is believed by many to be the main source of reference for the character of the Merlin who appears in Arthurian mythology. He is said to have been present at the battle of Arderryd where he saw a vision in the sky which sent him mad, and following his King's victory he left his service and retreated into the wilderness. Soon after, St. Columba came to Rhydderchs court at Dumbarton, replacing Merlin as he Kings counsellor. Columba is said to have ordered the capture of Merlin, whom he regarded as a threat to the stability of the emerging Celtic church, and when the hermit was finally found, he was forced to renounce his pagan beliefs. Myths and legends about Merlin and the boy King Rhyderrch Hael are numerous and varied, although it does seem clear that whatever the historical basis of them, in mythological terms, these characters form the basis of many Arthurian tales.

### CLOCHODERICK

Many sites throughout Strathclyde claim connection with Ryhderrch Hael, the most famous being Dumbarton Rock where the King is said to have held court after moving the capital of Strathclyde there from Carlisle. Dumbarton - the fort of the Britons - stood at the centre of his kingdom, in close reach of all four of the main tribes, and was easily defensible against both land- and sea-based attacks, making it the perfect fortress for the young King. After his victory at Arderryd, the druidic religion which had once held serious power over Kings, now found itself in chaos, and the Christian princes invited St.

*The stone of Clochoderick*

Kentigern to return his missionary work in Strathclyde. One of the most sacred sites associated with the Druids of this time was the stone of Clochoderick (Stone of Rhydderch), a huge volcanic boulder, some 12 feet high, which stands on a country road less than ten miles south of Kilmalcolm. This stone was thought to have been used by the druids as a place for judging criminals, although it has also been suggested as the site where Rhydderch was pronounced King. Others have theorised that the King raised the stone in memory of his victories, or that it marks the sight of his burial. Whatever the truth behind these legends, this impressive boulder still stands on a quiet country road, an enduring link to a distant past which is now all but forgotten.

# ST FILLANS FAYRE

*A mother and her sickly daughter brave the winter weather*
*in pilgrimage to the holy well of Saint Fillan...*

It was three weeks til Fillans Fayre and Elspeth was preparing to take her daughter Myrrin to bathe in the healing well. She had travelled there and back every Sunday for the last month.

It was dry, though bitterly cold, and mindful of this, Elspeth had wrapped little Myrrin in the largest of the blankets she kept in the home, warming it by the hearth before they left.

The walk from Barfillan to Killallan would take a little over half an hour and Myrrin would have to be carried there and back. Elspeth wrapped up a little bread and cheese for them to eat before the journey back home. The sun had not yet risen as they left.

"Look at the moon!" exclaimed Myrrin. "It's so bright!"

"We're very lucky to be up so early Mirri, we'll see the sun come up and say goodbye to the moon before she leaves."

Myrinn seemed very excited about this, and stared silently at the sky for a good part of the walk.

"I give up!" she said eventually.

"What?"

"I was trying to count stars but there's too many."

"Then don't try to count them all at once." explained Elspeth, "Just one at a time."

Myrrin sighed.

"When will I be well mother?"

"Soon Mirri, St Fillan will make you well."

Myrrin nodded sagely.

"Tell me about him again."

There was still some way to go to Killallan and Myrrin was restless.

"Well," said Elspeth "St Fillan was born over in Ireland, and he was the son of Prince Federach and Kentigerna, the Princess of Ulster. His father was of the Fiatach Finn."

"The who?"

"A noble people descended from the mighty warrior Fingal. However, Prince Federach was *not* such a noble man and he was not pleased when Kentigerna announced that she was with child. Worse, when Fillan was born, there was a stone in his mouth which Prince Federach thought was a sign from the old gods. So, he rode out into the forest with baby Fillan and just threw him into a lake."

"Even though he was only a baby?"

"Yes Myrrin."

"Was it like when I was baptised?"

"Not really Mirri. Your father and I were there with you by the water. Poor wee Fillan was just thrown in and then left by himself. Then Federach returned to Princess Kentigerna and told her that Fillan had been stolen away by the fair folk. And all the while, Fillan lay in the cold water of the lake."

"How did he not drown?"

"Ah! Angels stayed with little Fillan, and they sang to him. One of the angels held his left arm to keep him afloat. And that's why forever after, it glowed with holy light. It happened that Bishop Ibar was passing nearby, and found him by following the light and the singing of the angels. And when the Bishop found him, he took Fillan to the priory and brought him up in the christian faith. Now, Bishop Ibar, was a good friend of Princess Kentigerna's, and he explained that Federach had tried to kill her son. And so Kentigerna left Prince Federach, and she too became a christian. Both Fillan and his mother were missionaries and travelled all over Scotland."

"Where?" asked Myrinn, already knowing the answer.

"Once, when he was still a very young man, he journeyed to Killin. And when he arrived there, he found that the villagers were living in fear of a great wild boar. It had eyes red as burning coals, and tusks long enough to skewer three men at once. Right away, Fillan and his hound Dileas, set off into the woods to find the beast. He hunted for three days and three nights until he found it, sheltering under a rowan tree. Fillan, took his club in his left arm, and prayed to our lord for strength. And at this, the beast woke, turned and charged, roaring through the undergrowth. Quickly, Fillan brought his club down on the boar's head with all his strength, and he killed it stone dead."

"Good thing too." said Myrrin

"He travelled all across the country, carrying with him eight river washed stones. And these he used to cure the sick. When Fillan passed through our village on his travels, he liked it so much that he stayed and tended a little farm here for a time. Just over there."

Elspeth pointed off  towards the sunrise and Myrrin turned to look.

"I can't see it." said Myrrin

"It's just over the hill Mirri. And he would sit on a rock and children would gather round in the meadow to listen to his stories. In the same little field, scarcely a stone's throw away, is St Fillan's well."

"That's where we're going today!"

"Yes. That's where we're going today, because the water in the well helps to make children better. And after you've washed in the well, we'll hang a little thread on the nearby bush as a present for St. Fillan."

And sure enough, when they reached Killallan, Elspeth bathed Myrrin in

the well and then tied a thread from her shawl around the bush. There were already many other little threads or pieces of cloth tied there. Myrrin was quickly dried off and wrapped up in the blanket once more. Only after prayer and their meal, did they begin the walk back to Barfillan.

It was two weeks til Fillans Fayre.
Myrrin had not improved, and as the weather had been so changeable, Elspeth did not leave for the well til a little later in the day. There was almost no light in the day at all, a cold, grey dusk which encouraged almost everyone to stay indoors. But still, Elspeth prepared their bread and cheese and warmed their shawls by the fire before they left.
"Can I have a story on the way mother?"
"Of course you can Mirri. What would you like to hear? The tale of Lorne and Clutha? The story of Rhydderch Hael?"
"No. Father's *always* talking about Rhydderch Hael. Another Fillan story."
"You know them all too well Myrrin."
"I've forgotten."
"Do you remember Mirri, what happened the time St Fillan met the wolf?"
"No." she smiled.
"You do so. I've told you a dozen times."
"Two dozen!" laughed Myrrin "Tell me again."
"Well, Fillan had decided he wanted to build a little church, so that others would have somewhere to go to thank God for the gift of life they had been given. And he walked for many days until he found the perfect spot. It was a field which had not been tended to for many years. He had land for the foundations. There was a circle of stones standing nearby, and a little further across the way, a quarry. He had rocks for the walls. Beside the field was a forest. He had wood for the roof, and for the cross he would place inside his church. And at the corner of the field, was a tiny hut. He had somewhere to sleep and pray. From a local man, he bought oxen and an old plough to prepare the field. And then he began. At the end of the first hard day, he retired to his little hut.
When he woke in the morning, one of his oxen was dead. It had been killed by a wolf.
Fillan buried the ox, and continued ploughing the field, though now, with only one ox, it was much harder work. And when the day was done, Fillan left his ox and returned to his little hut to pray. But when he woke in the morning, his other ox lay dead. The wolf had killed again.
Fillan buried the poor creature, and then set off into the nearby wood. Deeper and deeper he went, into the trees, until the tangled knots of the branches blocked out the sun in the sky above. And there, in the middle of the forest in a little cave, was the wolf."

"Did Fillan kill the wolf mother?"

"No! Of course not. He simply wanted to explain to the wolf what damage he had done.

'Wolf.' he said 'Wolf you have killed my oxen and now I must plough the field by myself.'

'That is a pity.' said the wolf 'But you have strong arms to pull the plough with.'

'That is true. But I have a better idea.' said Fillan 'Will you not pull the plough for me?'

And at this the wolf howled with laughter.

'Tell me, why should I help you?'

'You have killed my oxen' said Fillan 'And that is as it should be. You are a wolf. And one of God's creatures.'

'I am no one's but my own.' replied the Wolf.

'We are all God's creatures.' said Fillan 'The oxen ploughed the field that I might lay stones and build a church to celebrate the life he has given us all.'

'I do not wish to celebrate with you and your God.'

'But you already do. When you run through the forests, when you howl at the skies, even when you killed my oxen, you are celebrating the life He has given you.'

'Yet because I have killed your animals, you cannot build your church.' smiled the wolf 'By living in my way, I have made your life more difficult.'

'Yes' said Fillan 'But that is part of the beauty of life. Understanding and appreciating the other lives around you. For although we are very different, we have one thing in common, the gift of life God has given us. You could help me with my ploughing, and then continue to celebrate life in your way. And I will continue to celebrate in mine.'

The wolf thought about this for a moment.

'I suppose I *should* be grateful to be living.' said the wolf 'And running. And howling.'

'That friend Wolf, is your decision.' said Fillan. And he left the dark of the forest behind him and walked back into the sunshine to begin ploughing his field.' "

"*Did* the wolf help Fillan?"

"He did Myrrin. The very next day he arrived to pull the plough for Fillan. He even helped him carry stones from the quarry to build the church walls. And soon, people came from all around to celebrate life in Fillan's little kirk. The Wolf and Fillan stayed good friends. Sometimes the wolf would come to the church to listen to Fillan's teachings, and at nights, Fillan would hear the wolf howling, and smile."

"Why did he smile mother?" asked Myrrin.

"Do you know what Fillan's name means Myrrin?"

"What does it mean?"

"It means 'little wolf'. He and his friend had more in common than the gift of life."

The rain started as they came to the well. Elspeth tied the thread to the branches of the bush. Myrrin joined Elspeth in a prayer, but she was not hungry and she slept and shivered all the way back to Barfillan.


It was the week before Fillans Fayre.

All through the week, Myrrin had slept, barely able to move or even to eat. Elspeth had not intended to travel to the well today, fearing Myrrin was now too ill to venture outside. But Myrrin herself had insisted, waking from her fever to ask when it would be time to leave.

So once again, Elspeth prepared them a little food for the return journey, and made sure Myrrin was wrapped up as warm as could be.

Myrrin was very quiet and still, but Elspeth spoke to her anyway, knowing she would enjoy the sound of her voice.

"Did you know Myrrin, that there is a Faerie Bridge over Netherwood way? Not too far from here.

And one day, while Fillan sat on his stone, telling stories to the smaller children, a man arrived on a horse.

'I am looking for a  man named Fillan.' he said

'I am Fillan. Can I help you?'

The man came down from his horse, and he looked very flustered and upset.

'You must help us' he said 'Our children are being spirited away across the Fairy Bridge. They say you hold some sway with the old Gods and the fair folk. Maybe you could talk to them, ask them to give us back our children.'

'It has been a  long time since I spoke to any of the old Gods. But of course I will do everything I can to help.'

Fillan took the man to his little house and gave him a small meal of bread and wine. They left the following day.

They rode from Barfillan, out to the Netherwood by Kilmacolm.

A group of villagers stood by the bridge, weeping for their lost children.

Fillan stopped to say a prayer with them, and then he crossed the bridge into the realm of the fair folk.

There was a troll fishing by the other side of the bridge.

'Where is the court of the Fairy Queen.' asked Fillan.

'You are in the court of Titania right now.' said the Troll

And the bridge and all the trees melted away, and there she sat, proud and beautiful.

'Queen Titania, I am Fillan, and I am here to ask for the return of the Kilmacolm children.'

'I am glad to meet you Fillan. But the children have crossed into faerie. They cannot go back.'

'Why did you spirit them here Lady?' asked Fillan.

'I enjoy their company. I love to see them play.' she said.

'Then come to our world and see them at play. Do not steal them away from their loved ones.'

Titania fell silent.

'We can no longer come into your world' she said. 'We cannot cross the bridge.'

'And that is why they must come to you?' asked Fillan.

Titania nodded.

'We stand by the bridge and we sing and we dance, and we hope they will come to see us.'

Fillan shook his head.

'Lady, you are above such trickery.'

And Titania knew that Fillan was right.

'There was a day when we did not *have* to trick people into crossing the bridge.'

And Titania, the proud queen of the fairies, cried a single tear.

'I bring them here to remind me of a world which is slipping away. We are forgotten, the fairer folk and the Old Gods are no longer welcome in your world. For that is what it has become, Your world, and that of your One God.'

Fillan smiled, and wiped the tear from the fairie queen.

'Lady, fairie will always be welcome in this part of the world. Always.'

And you know Mirri, that fairies are very fond of making agreements. Although they're never so keen to keep them. Fillan offered to make an agreement with them. If Titania returned all the children to the village, Fillan would make sure that people hereabouts would remember the old ways, and pay their respects to the fair folk.

As true as could be to her word, Titania let the village children cross back into Netherwood.

And truer still to his, Fillan made sure whenever anyone passed by the

fairy bridge, they would bow or courtsey to Titania, out of respect for how things used to be. And that's why, to this day, that fairy bridge is one of the few places in the whole kingdom, where the fair folk can cross into our world, or we into their's. If you're lucky when you pass, you can hear them singing. But you must not linger too long Mirri, for if you do, you'll start dancing to their songs, and dance straight across the bridge into Faerie. And not even St Fillan will be able to bring you back home."

Myrrin did not speak, but she smiled.

Elspeth bathed her in the water and tied a thread around the bush. She nodded to the other mothers who stood by, gazing sadly. Neither she nor Myrrin were hungry, so she gave the meal to a woman she knew from the nearby village.

And after prayer, they began the journey back to Barfillan.

It was January 19th, the day of Fillans Fayre. And Elspeth gathered Myrrin's shawl and the blanket she carried her in, and walked to Killallan through the first of the winter snow.

She came to the well, and, shaking snow from the branches of the bush, tied the shawl across it, the blanket, she folded and placed underneath. For a time she prayed, and then walked back towards Barfillan.

Elspeth knew St Fillan would protect Myrinn's soul.

# Saint Fillan

### Fillan's Early Life

After the victory of the Christian forces at the epic Battle of Arderyd, the growth of Christianity continued unabated in Scotland. The Celtic saints played a great part in this, Saint Columba having unified the many disjointed missions into a whole. For the next 150 years, the Christian word carried to the furthest reaches of Scotland. It was against this background that St. Fillan arrived in this country, some time around the early 700's.

Fillan, whose name literally translates as 'wolf cub' was born to Federach, a prince of the race of Fiatach Finn, and Kentigerna, a princess of Ulster. As the legend has it, he was born with a stone in his mouth. Federach saw this as a sign that this child was a curse to him, and threw him into a lake. However, Fillan was kept safe by angels, who watched over the child until he was discovered by Bishop Ibar, who raised him as his own child, in the Christian faith. Kentigerna kept a distant but watchful eye on her son, and was thankful to Ibar and his monks for caring for her son. Fillan's mother, too, would later become a missionary.

When Fillan landed on our shores, his mother and cousin Comgan accompanying him, they first settled in Lochalsh, in Wester Ross; later Fillan would travel to Glen Dochart, his mother retiring to Inch Cailleach, 'The Nun's Isle,' on Loch Lomond, where she died in 734 A.D.

### The Exploits of St. Fillan

To this day, stories are rife of Fillan's trials and adventures during the years when he was founding his missions. One such famous tale tells of a wolf who attacked Fillan's oxen while he was ploughing his fields, killing one; the wolf subsequently returned and allowed himself to be yoked. The animal would go on to aid Fillan in his ploughing, and help him build his priory. This tale is

*Saint Fillan at study*

*The visitor centre at Kilallan*

seen by some as an allegory for Fillan 'taming' the wilder elements of ancient Celtic culture.

Another legendary tale speaks of Fillan's battle against a fearsome boar in Killin. Fillan arrived there having parted company with St. Columba's biographer, Adoman, at Tyndrum, only to hear the town's tales of woe concerning this hideous beast, said to have 'tusks the size of plough shares.' Fillan set off into the forests to hunt down the boar, accompanied by his dog Dileas. Finding the enormous creature three days later, rooting beneath a rowan tree, Fillan held onto his simple wooden club as the boar turned on him and charged. Fillan brought the club down on the monster's head, killing it with one blow.

Tales of saints killing great beasts is far from uncommon; it is said that St. Columba defeated a mighty boar on Skye in a similar legend. These stories, true or not, play a part in idealising the saint figure, making him almost Godlike, and insuring that his name will carry on through history; such is the Ossian tradition of the hero in Celtic culture.

## Kilallan

The focal point of St. Fillan's labours in Scotland appears to have been Strathfillan in Perthshire, where a long stone known as St. Fillan's seat still remains. Nearby in a mill thought to have been built by the saint, seven holy stones, believed to have healing powers, are still preserved to this day.

Strathfillan is not the only site with strong links to the saint, and during his many travails throughout the country he seems to have founded churches in both Skelmorlie and, more importantly, in Kilallan, near Kilmacolm.

The name itself seems to be a corruption of Killfillan, i.e. Cella Fillani - the Cell of Saint Fillan. Here, on the Kilmacolm road to Houston, stands the ruins of a medieval church said to have been established by the saint during a long period of labour in the area.

Nearby, a large stone with a hollow in the middle is also remembered as St. Fillan's seat, the place were he is thought to have preached to a small number of followers. Such frequent and personal references to the saint certainly attest to the significance and impact of his work in the region.

However, the most famous shrine with a connection to the saint is St. Fillan's

Well, a stone's throw from Fillan's Seat in Kilallan. Here, under a rock, shaded by overhanging bushes, it is said that countrywomen would bring their weak and sickly children to be healed by the holy waters, leaving a small keepsake or offering hanging from the bushes. A similar practice was followed at Fillan's well in Skelmorlie; the plethora of wells associated with Fillan testifies to his reputation as a healer. In Kilallan, pilgrimages to the well went on until the end of the 1600's when the local minister, one Mr. Hutcheson, had the well filled with stones. Fillan's feast day was still celebrated with a fair on the same day for many years to follow,  and in the nearby village of Houston the parish church still bears his name.

St. Fillan's death is recorded on the 9th of January 777 (this, of course, is a date on the Julian calendar; on the Gregorian calendar, Fillan's death is marked as the 20th of January).

Fillan's followers preserve many relics associated with the saint; the most famous of these is the Mayne, the arm-bone of Fillan, which was kept in a silver case after his death. Such is the significance of this object that King Robert the Bruce requested it to be brought to him on the eve of the Battle of Bannockburn; however, the keeper in charge of the relic feared it would be damaged or lost, and brought the Bruce an empty case. As the king meditated over the case, praying for guidance during the coming battle, a mighty crack was heard from the silver box, and when opened it revealed the Mayne. The keeper , dumbfounded, admitted that he had not brought the bone with him. Whatever the truth of this story, the bone was undoubtedly carried into battle the next day, and the story may well have inspired the Scots to new bravery in this battle which liberated Scotland from the English rule.

LAST LORD
OF THE
WEST

*A century after the Norman conquest, great warlords battle for control in Scotland and the mighty Somerled of Argyll is chief among them...*

In the days of rebellion and conflict, when Scotland battled to become a nation, a mighty warlord named Somerled, the Thane of Argyll, ruled over the west of Scotland and all its islands. This wise and just man claimed descent from the house of the ancient Celtic kings, yet he had in the process of time found himself to be a somewhat over-mighty subject of two crowns. For while Malcolm IV, him that is descended from Macbeth, battled to secure the mainland, the Kings of Norway claimed the islands of West as their own, supported by the descendants of Viking invaders who had settled there.

For a long time Somerled watched as the two sides carved up his nation, dividing it amongst their noble men as they saw fit, giving the peasants a penny and charging them two. He realized that things could not continue as such for long and sensing that the day of war was close at hand, he summoned the council of the Isles to a meeting at the holy shrine of Saint Columba on Iona. Here, in the last great outpost of the Celtic Church, Thane was hailed as a protector of the old ways and a defender against the English puppet Malcolm, his spiteful wife and the invading Norse men who had proved victorious at Hastings less than a century before.

The news of the meeting at Iona spread quickly and soon all the lords of the islands were in attendance, as were many of the Thane's allies from Ireland and the coasts of the mainland where already Malcolm's men were starting to arrive. They gathered around the Stone of Destiny, which stood there long before it resided at Scone, and debated long over what they should do. After three days of discussions, the lords could still not reach an agreement as to which course of action they should take. Somerled was strongly of the belief that they must tackle Malcolm head on, in order to usurp him from the throne and take back Scotland before it fell into the hands of the English nobles. Such a motion was supported by Somerled's most loyal supporters, including one of his oldest allies Earl Maceth who had until recently spent twenty eight years in a prison in Roxburgh. But many of the other members of the council, including members of the Thane's own family, thought it better to negotiate a treaty, or worse still, to seek help from the Kings of Norway. Eventually the young Lord Campbell of Craignish, who had long been under the tutelage of Somerled, spoke up in defense of his friend's plans:
"For too long we have watched as our lands are taken from us and our kinsmen treated like cattle. The wise lord Somerled is right, Malcolm must

be faced on his own ground and now is the time to do so. Scotland belongs to the Scots, not to some puppet King who answers to the English. We must act now, less we debate so long as to give the enemy time enough to arrive at Iona herself."

Such noble and patriotic words swayed the council and plans were made for the raising of an army and the building of enough ships to carry them to the mouth of the Clyde. For this purpose Somerled spoke as follows:
"Let the word go forth to every man of the Western lands that Somerled, Thane of Argyll is raising an army to go forth against Malcolm, King of the Scots. The purpose of such a force is the preservation of the lives and freedom of every man, woman and child in the West and beyond, lest our land be over run by greedy nobles who want nothing more than to destroy our way of life."

Winter was setting in by the time the force was assembled and thus many months were spent training and preparing the ships. From all around they came, the men of Lorne, Mull, Loch Sween, the lands of the firth and even Ireland. In all, four thousand men and a total of one hundred and sixty galleys. Somerled himself had spent the many months in seclusion with the monks on Iona who had advised him greatly over the years, both on political matters, and the art of warfare. The Thane had also spent time preparing his sons for their first battle and the young Lord Campbell, who was treated by them like a brother, and like a son by their father.

Spring finally arrived and the troops broke camp and boarded their ships. Word went out to the islands that Somerled's army was ready to move and a final blessing was given by the monks of Iona:
"May God be with you in your quest Somerled, Thane of Argyll. Yours is a just fight and is seen as such in the eyes of our lord. We pray that the wind will always be at your back and hope that calm seas will guide you to safe harbours and a glorious victory."
 Thus it was that in the spring of the eleven hundred and sixty fourth year of our lord, one hundred and sixty of the brave warlords galleys, filled with four thousand of the finest warriors in the west, set sail for the firth of the Clyde and a battle for their nations freedom.

Clear skies and fast winds brought them to the sound of Islay when they were at sea scarcely a day. Ships from all around the inner Hebrides joined them as they moved swiftly southwards to the Mull of Kintyre, and torches lit up all the lands that they passed, signaling support for the old ways and the Thane of Argyll. Within three days they passed Toward point and entered the firth of the Clyde. Unknown to them the supporters of the King who

manned the ancient Tor at Ardgowan had spotted the fleet and dispatched riders to Renfrew to inform Walter Fitz Allan, he that was the first of the Stewart line, ancestor of the Bruce and servant of Malcolm. Similarly the Cluniac monks of Innerkip sent word to Paisley and Glasgow, warning that the warriors of the Celtic church were hurrying to burn their churches. It was thought that by spreading such lies, a greater force might be raised against Somerled and his men.

As night fell on their third day out of Iona, the great fleet passed the Kempock point and the Thane could not help but marvel at the strange sight of the stone which stood atop it.  Little did he know that just as they had passed Ardgowan under observation, so too now did they pass the Kempock stane. A mysterious place, guarded by many a weird individual. And one such person watched the mighty galleys pass by the small fishing croft below and round the point  where  they were greeted with the age old safe harbour of Saint Laurence, nestled within which lay the village of Greenock. Upon laying eyes on the lush green bay, Somerled proclaimed: "Take heart men, our journey on the waves is at an end and battle must surely be close at hand. Many a man has spoke well of the herring in these parts, thus let us land here and tonight we shall feast in the village by the bay beneath the sacred oaks."

So it was that the galleys of Somerled dropped anchor, mooring from the meikle stone where later the kirk would stand, all the way to the Mairchean. Never before had the river played host to such a vast brigade of ships. In the village there was much commotion and celebration, for while they had recently come under the feu of Walter Fitz Allan, they desired the preservation of their way of life and a freedom from taxes by foreign nobles. In their eyes no man could own the land any more than they could own the air they breathed.

That night the warriors feasted with the villagers and all in attendance were in the highest of spirits; the men of Somerled anxious for the great battle that lay ahead, the people of Greenock feeling a sense of pride that they were playing host to such a mighty and just army. As the celebrations continued, Somerled noticed a band of  men dressed in simple robes lurking at the edge of the feast, watching him silently. After inquiring about them, he learned that they were followers of Saint Blaine and had long maintained a small but ancient order here. Learning this Somerled spoke thus:
"Welcome followers of Blane. Many a time have I visited your patrons shrine on the Isle of Bute. I am told by the monks of Iona that he was a

wise man indeed, with a wide knowledge of the old ways, especially those conducted in these parts. I would ask that you pray to him to give blessing for our quest. Now come, join us."

The monks blessed the Thane then cautiously approached the tables, eating little and saying even less. But Somerled noticed that one of their number remained on the outskirts, a hood hiding his face. A long time did he wait there and when finally the feast ended and the warriors began to retire, still he stood their, failing to leave with the other monks. Eventually Somerled approached him:

"Why did you not leave with your kin brother?"

"Mine is not their cause. I may dress like them, but our paths lead in different directions. But you, Somerled, yours is a cause for which I feel much passion. This land must remain free. On that much depends. You have my blessing, and the blessing of Clutha. Never have I seen her give such a safe passage to so many ships. The Gods of old are with you Thane of Argyle. But beware, there is one amongst you who does not share your passion. Fare thee well."

And at that the hooded figure retreated into the shadows. Somerled watched bewildered for a moment. Too much wine perhaps? Perhaps.

When morning broke, Somerled held a council of war. It was decided that as much of their force was on foot, that they would be divided into three sections. One would take the coastal route towards what was expected to be the main battlefield. The other would head across the higher ground of Strathgryffe and the final group would take up position as reinforcements. The Thane would lead the forces going through Strathgryffe aided by the young lord Campbell, the Earl Maceth would follow the coastal route and Somerled's sons would remain in reserve, lest both father and his heirs be lost. Thus the great forces set out from the small fishing village, hope in their heart and strength in their arms.

By mid day, the Thane passed the old church of Saint Fillan and his scouts reported that the enemy had been sighted North of Houston, having been forced onto the higher ground by Maceth. Somerled rode forth to battle, swiftly followed by the anxious young Campbell. Maceth's forces moved south from the river and the two forces met on an open field. And here they engaged the enemy, charging the smaller force of Walter Fitz Allan's household knights, a well armed band who where fiercely loyal to the King. Many fell in the first charge and Somerled fought hard to drive a wedge between the enemy. God was with them and armour was no match for men fighting a cause. Fitz Allan lost many a good man that day and finally by early evening Somerled encountered Maceth on the field, the

young Campbell still at his side:

"Victory must surely be at hand my friends. What say you?"

Maceth gave him a sombre look, almost as if he had seen a ghost, and Somerled Thane of Argyle turned to face the young Campbell who already had his sword drawn. The mighty warlord moved to attack then felt the stab from behind. Campbell lunged forward, grabbing his master's body as he stabbed forward at the assassin Maceth, killing him with one clean cut.

The news of the Thane's death at the hands of Maceth spread quickly, and the loss of their mighty leader through betrayal struck a greater blow to the army than any Fitz Allan could have managed. The tide turned quickly and as night fell, the few hundred warriors that remained retreated back to Greenock under the leadership of Campbell and the sons of Somerled. The sympathy of Clutha was with them, and calm waters sped them quickly back home, tears in the eyes of all those who saw them pass.

And some say that the followers of Somerled later returned to the place where he fell in secret and marked the site with a cross made by the finest artisans in all the western lands. No-one knew whence this cross had come from and in later it became known as the Barrochan cross, standing as it did near the old house of Barrochan near Kilmalcolm, before being removed to the museum of Paisley where it remains to this day.

# THANE OF ARGYLL

*A warrior from the Western Isles*

"The history of the west from the mid twelfth century to the first war of independence is largely the history of the House of Somerled."

G.W.S. Barrow.

## LORD OF THE ISLES

In 1153, Malcolm IV, only a twelve-year-old boy at the time, succeeded David I as king of Scotland. The Scotland of the twelfth century was still very much a feudal kingdom, with warlords wielding much power over large parts of the land. One of the greatest problems the young king faced was the dispute over control of Argyll and the Western Isles. Many of the settlers in these areas were of Viking stock, who divided allegiance equally between the Scots and Norse crowns.

In 1098, Edgar, then king of Scotland, had signed a treaty with the Norwegian king Magnus Bareleg, which confirmed the islands west of Kintyre as Norwegian; however, the Norwegians were largely unhappy with this, claiming Norse rule over not only these islands, but also those in the Firth of Clyde, including Arran, Bute and the Cumbraes.

Despite the weakening of their political influence in the area, the Norwegians still attempted to take a strong hand in Scottish affairs. This was achieved mainly through the Thane of the region, who was, in essence, the voice of the king of Norway. The Thane's involvement in this affair caused a kind of constitutional crisis, however; both the Scots and Norse rulers claimed the Thane as their own representative in the

area. It would only be a matter of time, however, before this matter would come to a head, and conflict was already looming on the horizon.

### SOMERLED

At this time, the Thaneship was held by one Somerled Macgillebrigte who, though of Norse descent, was growing weary of his Norwegian masters. He was mainly instrumental in causing a revival of Celtic culture, throwing off the vestiges of Scandinavian tradition, and drawing on the ancient Scots-Irish links. For too long he had considered himself too powerful a leader to be the subject of two kings.

Somerled spent a great deal of his reign cementing his power by intermarrying his family with powerful landowners on the Scots isles; by 1153, his power base was strong enough to warrant a rebellion against king David.

Due to troubles in the Isle of Man, the Norwegians had all but lost their hold on Scotland. Indeed, it was doubtful whether they could have interceded had they wanted to; Somerled had become too powerful for them to command.

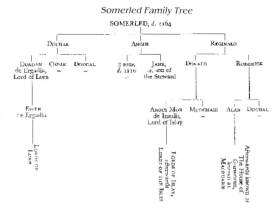
*Somerled Family Tree*

By 1163, Somerled's contempt for the crown had become so great he saw fit to commit what was surely seen as the ultimate indignity; he attempted to have Iona, at the time Scotland's most revered holy site, placed under the jurisdiction of Ireland. At this time, it would seem that Somerled saw himself as more than Lord of the Isles, and began to think about making a play for the Scottish crown.

### WAR WITH THE MAINLAND

"The King came with his army to Glasgow in order to give battle to Somerled, who marched up the south side of the Clyde, leaving his galleys at Greenock."
-Anderson

England's recent attempts to invade Ireland, and the strong links they maintained with the Scots crown, made Somerled fear for the future of what he now considered his native land. In 1164, the truce officially broke down between Somerled and king Malcolm, and the Thane, gathering all his forces, sailed up the Firth of the Clyde with a fleet of 160 Birlins, oak ships adapted from the Viking style by Somerled himself. These he landed at the bay of St. Lawrence where Greenock Harbour now stands.

Accounts of subsequent events vary, although it seems that the Thane met here with a large number of Irish auxiliaries before making his way to face the king's forces.  One account claims that when word spread that Somerled had landed, there was panic in the streets of Glasgow and the citizens took refuge in the Cathedral in fear for their lives. They need not have worried, for King Malcolm sent his most formidable warrior to face the rebel, Walter Fitz Allan, Steward of Renfrew who brought with him his famed household knights. There is much debate as to where the two great forces met, although it is widely accepted that it was somewhere east of Kilmacolm, though no further than Paisley or Renfrew. Yet wherever it was, the battle did not last long, and Somerled seems to have fallen early in the skirmish.

"And in the first cleft of battle the baleful leader fell. Wounded by a thrown spear, slain by the sword, Somerled died."
-Carmen de Morte Sumerledi

It has been suggested that the Thane was betrayed by one of his own, most likely one of his nephews, who had been enlisted by the King as an assassin. Upon hearing of his death, Somerleds forces dissipated, returning to Greenock to reclaim their ships and making a swift escape back to Argyle.
It is unclear what happened to the Thanes corpse after this, although some stories suggest that it was taken to the king before been taken to Iona for burial. Another tradition maintains that the Barrochan cross, a Celtic monument in the style of the Govan School which once stood on a hill behind Langbank, marked the site of the Thanes tomb. Whatever the truth, this mighty warlords attempts to free Scotland from external influence foreshadowed the great wars of independence which were to dominate the following centuries.

*A celtic cross in the Govan style*

## GALGAEL TRUST

Somerled and his fleet of longships are still powerful symbols of cultural freedom, a group in Glasgow aim to build a Birlinn.

The Galgael Trust is based in Govan and was set up by unemployed people who wanted to take action to solve the problems faced by their communities and work to reverse the trend of environmental, social and cultural degradation, particularly in Scotland. To this end, the trust aims to unite the entire community in the construction of a Norse Longhouse and a Birlinn. Around this work, a better sense of cultural inheritance and a respect for the land and its ecology will be built. The Longhouse Project was inspired by Govan's hogback stones, 10th Century tombstones carved in the shape of a longhouse. Intricate animal carvings adorn many of the end gables. These unique stones evolved in a number of Gaelic-Norse settlement areas of the British Isles, revealing a fusion of the Norse and Gaelic carving style and cultures and a shared reverence for the natural world.

Once the Birlinn has been built, it will set sail on a millenial voyage that will circle Scotland. The Birlinn represents the journey that must be made from present social hardships to an improved quality of life, a symbol of cultural and spiritual renewal.

Visit the Govan Boat and the Longhouse behind Govan Old Parish Church, phone for more information on 0141 445 6886.

*A 12ft model of the Galgael Birlinn at Portsoy Traditional Boat Festival June 1999*

# Walking to the Kirk

*A forest God sees the passing of the old ways*
*as the new religion takes hold...*

The walk to the Auld Kirk is long, twice as long on the way back with sundays meal still miles away and only bread and wine to line the empty bellies of the congregation.

Yes, the walk home is hard, but it is safer than the early morning journey. In wintertime the road is darker than the devil's own heart and careless pilgrims may find themselves lost in the empty black of the Glen. Or worse, wandering in the forest of Ravenscraig. This is why we must all stay close together, why we sing the hymns as we walk.
Pan, The Old Lord of all the Forests, sometimes comes to visit the spirits of the Ravenscraig Trees, and he is not happy when we pass him by. On his last visit to these parts he caused a goodly commotion.

It was a Sunday in advent, and Pan was visiting all the forest sprites to see that they were making preparations for the Winter Solstice, the festival of light which marked the end of the old pagan year.
And as Pan stood talking with the Faerie Chieftan, he heard singing echoing up from the glen. Through the trees he could see the flickering of our candles as we walked toward the Kirk.
"What's this?" he asked "Are these people come to honour The Forest Lord?"
The Faerie Chief was a little embarassed.
"No Lord." he said "The folk walk to their worship, the kirk some way along the glen."
"Church? They walk through my forest to church? We shall see about that."
And Pan charged all the spirits to stop the procession through the glen.
"They must not pass without first honouring me." he said.
And all the land obeyed his order.

The procession came to Christs Well, where every Sunday, those who were thirsty or ill would drink of the healing waters on their way. But the vines had heard Pan, and they choked the well so none could drink. And the grass snakes had heard Pan, and they slithered round the spring, hissing at any who tried to get near enough to clear the vines.
The pilgrims walked on.

The wild cats which live on the moors had heard Pan, and they came down into the Glen, their eyes shining from between trees, growling as

the procession walked on. And the leaves had heard Pan and they leaped down from the trees to hide the forest path.
The pilgrims walked on.

The wind had heard Pan, and came whistling through the trees, blowing out all the candles, darkening the Glen. And the ravens had heard Pan, and they flew up to blacken the sky, just in case the sun rose.
The pilgrims linked hands and sang all the louder. And a candle burned bright in the Auld Kirk guiding them safely through the dark. They walked on.
"Enough!" cried Pan "I will stop them myself."
And he played his pipes, those pipes which have long lured men into the trees.
They walked on, past the trees, through the glen, and into the Kirk.
Pan played his pipes til the last of them was safely inside, his tunes and charms echoing down into the valley, and into silence.

And since then, whenever he is hereabouts, he will try to stop the churchgoers as they pass through the glen. Though he visits less and less, we must still be wary of him as we pass along the way, for if you don't stay close, he might steal you away into the trees.

# THE AULD KIRK

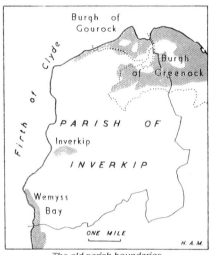

*The old parish boundaries*

"In the year 1170 Baldwin de Bigres, sheriff of Lanark, gave a grant of land to the monks of Paisley Abbey, consisting of the Pennyland between the rivulets of Kip and Daff. Eighteen years afterwards there is evidence that the church was already built; the spot chosen was that occupied now by the old churchyard. For 600 years it stood, before age and inevitable decay brought about its final destruction. For four centuries it was the only church between Kilmacolm and Largs. It was not until the year 1589 that a petition was presented by 'the fishers of Greenock' for a church of their own. They complained of the long road they had to travel to and from the Kirk at Inverkip, leaving no time for rest on the Sabbath 'according to Goddis institution'. A year or two afterwards authority was given by royal charter to erect a church in Greenock - that known as the Old West church. In 1801 the old church of Inverkip was replaced by the present one which faces the main road and was built in simple classic style."

- the Rev. William Crawford.

*The Kirk today.*

# The Duchal Ghost

*A holy brother, once in God's service, turns to the ways of darkness after his ingracious death and besets the home of a good and noble knight...*

It was full dark by the time our strange visitor came knocking on the door of the gatehouse; too late for any reasonable man to be up and about. Yet still he knocked, and knocked, and knocked, till he would have even woken Tuck, whose snores could drown out cannonfire. Seven good men and myself still walked the castle walls at that hour; taking care of business which needed tending.

It transpired that this man of the woods had come to Ardgowan to visit Sir Thomas Randolph; how he was acquainted with the knight he could not say, but no matter how important the reason for his visit, it would not be possible till morning. I told him the same, which he took in good graces, and one of the men (I think Green) bid him sit out our watch with us, and take something hot into his stomach.

At this, the elderly man brightened, and took great happiness in sitting by the fire listening to tales of soldiering and ribaldry. When the lads' tales of bravery dried up, however, as most tales of bravery will do eventually, the mood turned to the otherworldly, and the boys took turns telling our guest of the apparitions they had witnessed on nightwatch within the castle walls. At this, he took on a sombre caste, and asked the men if they knew anything of the nearby castle of Duchal, and of its dark history. When blank faces and head-shakes greeted him, he stood amongst them and began his story. To this day I know not whether it be true or false, but no matter; it stays with me still, and I regard this as important.

I have penned it here in order that someone else may read it; anyone will do. I have done my part; my inkwell is almost dry and my wife calls me.
Aymer de Valance
Governor of Scotland
1305

Our tale begins in 1296, when men were simpler, and never more so than among the holy men of the Abbey of Paisley; but it would seem that one among these noviciates was not so pious as his brothers would have believed, for this certain monk was not satisfied with the carnal forbearance and life of prayer thrust upon his by his vocation, and sought less spiritual pleasures. It seems this monk would escape his simple room at night and seek out the company of local young hot bloods. Together with these rapscallions, he would engage in sports and pastimes completely unbecoming of his chosen lifestyle as a man of God.

To this day it is not quite clear exactly what the monk did which was so reprehensible, but nevertheless he was found out and excommunicated

with all speed, and later died still with this black sin on his name.

In any other case this may be where our tale would end. However, it would certainly seem that the good brother was not yet finished on the earthly plane, and began making ghostly visits to the Abbey; and believe me, reader, if the sinful monk's life was lived in wicked disregard of the sanctity of his station, his deathly appearances had a decidedly more evil purpose.

Shortly after the monk's burial (whether he was granted a funeral on the sacred ground of the Abbey is not clear, although such a heinous sinner would no doubt be denied eternal rest in consecrated earth), stories began to spread around the Abbey about a shadowy monkish figure who stalked through the halls and cloisters at night, shocking the fear of Death into his former brothers under Christ with his ghastly appearance and stench of brimstone. To make matters worse, the disgraced brother was not content with frightening the residents of the Abbey half to death, he would also try to tempt them into sin, carrying on his ungodly ways into the afterlife. The holy fathers told each other tales of how they had witnessed this apparition, and all realised the seriousness of this spirit and the harm he posed the order. The Abbey was thrown into confusion by this terrible haunting, and it was decided by the brothers that severe action would be taken to rid themselves of the malefic entity.

What arcane method they utilised to exorcise this wandering sinful spirit is still unknown to us; perhaps a long and convoluted ritual replete with prayer and sackcloth; perhaps merely the steadfast Bell, Book and Candle, tools of holy men since times forgotten. No matter; for by whatever means, the monks succeeded in persuading the wandering ghost to restrict his mischiefs only to those who were with him when he committed the terrible sins which resulted in his defrocking.

Records of this black period at the Abbey are thin at best (and with good reason; no doubt the brothers would soonest forget this dark addition to their ranks), and so the only clear fact we can ascertain is that the monks' methods to banish their wandering brother from their walls were successful; they were never again troubled by apparitions of the darkest kind. Indeed, their efforts to send this spirit to bother his co-accused seem to have been very successful indeed, for the next time the spirit was seen by mortal men was in Kilmacolm, where he apparently took up a new home in the house of Duchal, which was, at this time, the family home of a prominent knight by the name of Duncan de Lyle.

Immediately the black monk's work began within the walls of Duchal, although he did not restrict himself to the castle walls; his robed form was viewed by many in the fields and gardens surrounding the house, as well as roaming its rooms and hallways, assuming a foul air, and as palpable, it seemed, as any man. Nor was our nefarious brother only about his deeds within the hours of darkness; he seemed unconcerned as to whether he was viewed in the light of day by mortal man, this spectre who brought the unknown with him, tucked into the folds of his cassock.

At first the monk's purpose with the family of Duncan de Lyle was unclear, for he seemed to have made a new home in Kilmacolm simply to cause mischief and cause much gnashing of teeth. He would sit on the barn or outhouse roof, perching there for all the world like a great and evil sinister crow, his visage ever hidden from the eye, and calling out halloos to all and sundry who would pass his way, insulting them with a barrage of the foulest and most disgusting language they had ever heard, and some of them women and children of a kindlier disposition, at that. The Knight and his band of faithful retainers would attempt to shoot arrows at the dark figure, but their missiles would shrivel in the air as they approached the unholy brother, almost as if dipped in molten lead. At this provocation, the monk would leap into their midst, grabbing at one or two of the archers with freakish strength, shaking them as if to break every bone in their bodies. Surely the good Knight despaired at his home and peace being invaded by this hellion.

The dark brother was apparently the better of every good fighting man within Duchal's walls, and would beat them every one into submission with his hellish strength. However, one resident within the castle's walls could apparently hold his own in hand-to-hand combat; none other that Duncan's son. The young man would wrestle with the monk for hours, neither one giving an inch, and this was fair strange.

Who among us can pretend an understanding of the ways of death, or what lies beyond it? Not I. For this reason I do not offer explanation of what occurred next in this black tale, only relate to you, my friend, the tale as it was told to me; as, I hope fervently, you will tell it some day hence.

The monk in black garb made his true purpose in setting up home in Duchal Castle all too clear one wintry night, when the knight De Lyle was seated by a roaring fire in the castle's kitchens, his entire family and his

many friends and compatriots around him. All of a flurry, the monk appeared in their midst, belabouring all with fists and feet and poker, and the good men and women ran for fear of their lives, until the only two combatants by the kitchen's great stone hearth were the young laird and his pitch-dark nemesis.

The poor young man's family, taking up positions at the oaken kitchen door, heard scuffling and wailing and a great pandemonium all through the long night, fearing to open wide the door until all was quiet, when the morning sun shone through the castle windows. When they did, they found the bold knight's young son dead on the floor, a look of terror on his face; of the black monk, there was never any sign, ever again.

There are those who say that the young man brought his fate upon himself; that he, as one of the scurrilous fellows who sinned with the monk, was haunted and eventually murdered for a reason, albeit a strange and unearthly one.
But people say many things.
Perhaps this is just a story.

# DUCHAL CASTLE

*Remains of Duchal Castle*

The ruins of Duchal Castle are to be found halfway along the road connecting Greenock and Kilmacolm. The barony was in possession of the De Lyles as early as 1165, although it is believed the castle itself was built during the thirteenth century, and named for the murky water of the area, Duchal meaning literally 'black water'.

The first mention of the De Lyle family names one Radulfus (or Ralph) De Lyle, descended from Raoul, a famed Teutonic knight and companion to William the Conqueror.

At points throughout Scottish local history, members of the De Lyle family are seen to play many parts; as witnesses to the Charter of Paisley Abbey and certain agreements relating to Inverkip Church, and also as sympathisers to the cause of William Wallace.

Curiously, Paisley Abbey is the starting point for one of the most infamous chapters in the history of Duchal Castle; the tale of the Duchal Ghost. The tale is recorded in the medieval chronicle at Lanarcost Priory, and was first told to knights stationed at Ardgowan Castle during the English occupation. The story has been retold many times since the unusual events of 1296, though few facts, if any, have changed to this day. One strange interpretation, however, suggests that the black monk who haunted Duchal's walls was, in fact, a baboon brought to this country by a knight of the Crusades.

King James IV would reside at Duchal Castle whenever he visited Renfrewshire. However, in 1489, during a rebellion which involved Lord Lyle, the garrison at Duchal was attacked by the King's army. Among the heavy artillery the King's men brought with them was the great cannon Mons Meg, which can be seen to this day at Edinburgh Castle. This show of force may well have

*The Porterfield Crest*

convinced Lyle to surrender himself rather than face bombardment.

The Porterfield family were made Lairds of Duchal in 1544, and found themselves embroiled in the Renfrewshire family feuds which took place in the fifteenth and sixteenth centuries. During this time, the castle was occupied, partially burned down and finally returned to its rightful owners.

Duchal Castle was abandoned in 1710, when the Porterfields moved to a more desirable location. Since then, the castle has gradually slipped into the surrouding waters, very little of its structure remaining today. In addition to the remnants to be seen from the Kilmacolm road, pieces of the castle can be found in Paisley Museum, in particular what seems to be a relief of a 'Green Man.' Nearby Chapel Farm is the site of the old Lyle chapel, where the families of Duchal worshipped and were buried. The side

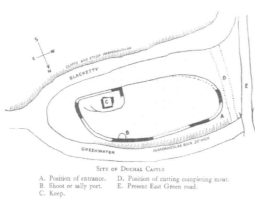

SITE OF DUCHAL CASTLE
A. Position of entrance.    D. Position of cutting completing moat.
B. Shoot or sally port.      E. Present East Green road.
C. Keep.

*Map of the castle grounds*

chapel still existed in 1633. Close to this is the spring of crystal clear water, presumably an ancient holy well, which was probably used for baptisms and christenings.

The burial vaults of the Porterfields of Duchal has a curious anagram inside:

"This anagram unfold - my buildar sall
His name quha vil into this sentence seik
Till flie the il make guid report of al
Guiliame sal find Porterfield of that ilk.
Zeirs sevintie five to live he livit and more
But nov for ay livs with ye Gods but vo."

A strange epitaph, the riddle is as yet unsolved, although the solutions is said to be carved into the back of the tomb.

# The Tower

*In the time of Wallace and The Bruce, Scottish forces lay seige*
*to a castle occupied by the English...*

### The Parish of Innerkip - May 1307

A good country is like a good castle; built on strong foundations with the ability to defend itself. At least that's what William used to say. Now Scotland, for her part has both of these in half measures. Sure we can fight, as many a battle will testify, and we can claim this land as our own with a rich culture and a strong sense of independence. Yet it still seems as if the mortar between the bricks has come loose somewhere. Consider this; it is the 1307th year of our lord and after for over twenty years now Scotland has battled for her right to nationhood. Towns have been put to the sword, wives widowed, sons left fatherless and yet we remain bound.

Now forget the nobles and the Kings. Where is the common man in all this? I am Jamie Macintosh, a Scotsman born and bred, marching with men from all over this nation, under the banner of a Scottish noble who holds as many titles in England as he does here. We have a King of our own, and a country of our own. Yet it is riddled with English forces, with whom he continues to treat. I am no better off than I was ten years ago, nor are any of the other serfs I march with. So one has to wonder exactly why it is that we are fighting, and how strong this tower really is.

I am an archer in the service of Sir James Douglas and for two days now, since our victory at Loudon Hill we have, at the behest of the king, pursued one Philip de Mowbray, commander of the English forces. And now we have come to hills behind Finnoch bog, looking down on Spango valley just as the sun sets. The word from the front is that Mowbray has taken refuge in the Castle of Ardgowan, a move which had always been anticipated by those in command. And now as I look down into the valley, I understand why.

The tiny village of Innerkip sits nestled between the wooded hills, overlooking a small bay on the firth of the Clyde, on the other side of which lie the foothills of the Clyde. It is a beautiful sight, and as the sun casts it last rays down upon the houses, dipping behind the far away hills, I cannot help but think how blessed the villagers are. And then I let my gaze wander to the right and I catch my first glimpse of the tower. Black as ash it stands, peering out from the trees, the smoke of war surrounding it, a great blight on a perfect landscape. Something unwanted, unnatural. Water lies on three sides, creating a small peninsula which is joined to the mainland by a heavily guarded road. After all, this is the chief English

garrison of the Renfrewshire Barony. Around the main structure stand several wooden sheds and huts, and through the trees I can just make out the shape of another large structure, though what it is I cannot tell. No, the villagers of Innerkip are nor blessed, they are cursed.

We make camp in the hills. Fires have been forbidden, even though we are almost in plain sight of the enemy and it is unlikely that our force of nearly ninety archers will have gone unnoticed. So for supper we are forced to eat our pre-cooked rations cold, washed down with a mug of warm cider. After an hour or so Sir James addresses the men, asking for volunteers for a night raiding party. It would seem that the commanders intend to lay siege to Ardgowan. But Sir James wants more accurate information before we commit to battle. Four raise their hands, including myself and Sir James decides to send us all. We are ordered to capture some local and bring him back for questioning, and where possible avoid contact with the enemy.

As darkness descends and the last light on the horizon fades, we take up our bows and head into the forest, led, due to virtue of age, by myself. Before too long we come across a dirt track which seems to head in the direction of the village, and deciding that there will be little or no traffic at this hour, we follow it. Yet despite the relative safety afforded by the midnight hour, I feel incredibly anxious, clutching nervously at my bow. The woods here do not seem to take kindly to visitors, and during our short trip to the outskirts of the village I am unable to shake the feeling that I am being watched.

The two short streets of the village are entirely deserted and we find no sign of either serf or soldier. We decide to head to the end of the track we seems to meet with the main road to the castle. Yet as we creep through the darkness, the light of a candle suddenly becomes visible a short distance away, moving in our direction. In a flash I bring an arrow to the string and take aim. And then, just I am about to loose the dart, I hear the singing. The particular song is hardly one an Englishman would be found singing, so our midnight wanderer must be one of the villagers. We lie in wait for him, taking cover behind a cartload of hay. And then we pounce. He puts up little struggle, a fact probably explained by the stench of whisky on his breath. Reluctantly I knock him unconscious, and then before any one is any the wiser we retreat back into the forest. Hopefully he will provide us with what we are looking for.

As morning breaks, Sir James and the other commanders have already begun questioning the prisoner. It would seem that he is a carpenter from the village who is employed by the garrison. He, along with some twenty or so others, most of whom are Irish slave workers, have been working on a large siege engine which is being constructed in the grounds of the

castle. However yesterday, after the arrival of Sir Philip the workers were all sent home and work was halted. The garrison was put on full alert and reinforcements were sent for. After this, the man declared that he knew little more that would be of use to Sir James, and when asked to estimate the number of soldiers he replied only that the castle was stuffit full of Englishmen.

By noon our scouts reported that the Castle appeared to have been readied for a siege, and there remained little doubt now that the English were aware of our presence. Sir James announced that he intended to attack before nightfall, less Mowbray attempted to escape or reinforcements arrived in such numbers that would render any engagement impossible. The plan is to take control of the outer ring of buildings first, and then if possible use the enemies own siege engine against them. To this end Sir James splits the force into three units of roughly thirty men in each. Two of these groups will man the beaches on either side of the main road to the castle, using burning arrows to set the outer buildings ablaze. The third group, in which I had been posted, will then rush the peninsula and hopefully take control of the work yard and begin the siege proper.

As dusk settles over the little village, an eerie silence permeates the air and not a soul is to be seen on the road as we march towards the tower. They are scared. And they are not alone. Coming closer now to the castle I catch a better glimpse of it through the trees. It looks strong, but will it hold? We shall see soon enough. The outer gates have been abandoned by the time we reach them and Sir James seems pleased that we are able to take our intended positions without any early skirmishes.

As I stand in the line between the two gate posts which mark the peninsula, I sling my bow onto my shoulder and unsheathe my short sword fearing I will be fighting the enemy at close hand. On the beach the fires are lit and the archers take the arrows to the string. Then the signal is given, and it begins.

Within minutes the whole area around the tower seems engulfed in a thick black smog, out of which comes the first wave of arrows from the bows of the enemy. Another hail from our side, and then we are ordered to charge. Time appeared to stand still, and what seemed like a short distance minutes before, seems like miles now. The arrows fly past my ear, and before we have even crossed the first ten yards, three have already fallen. Finally the first line reach the outer huts, although little can be seen through the smog. I take cover behind an empty barrel, stealing a moment to catch my breath. And then in a flash the enemy is upon me. He thrusts forward with a pike, cracking the barrel in two as I roll out the way. I scramble to my feet and lunge towards him, sword raised above my head. The clash is quick and brutal, leaving only one of us standing. Peering

through the smoke I catch a glimpse of the others from my brigade taking cover from another hail of arrows. We quickly set up a makeshift barricade across the road with whatever we can find, providing cover for archers on the beach to move in closer. Moving round to the east side of the yard, I catch my first glimpse of the siege engine. Standing two stories tall, with a catapult mounted on the top and an iron forged battering ram, it stood looming over the stable block. However the English had obviously foreseen our attempts to use it, and had attempted to scuttle the siege engine by severing the catapult. The battering ram seemed to function good enough, though the structure seemed somewhat fragile. We moved it into position and on Sir James orders began our assault on the outer gate. By this time the archers were close enough to take aim inside the main walls, and several fires had broken out in the tower itself.

Ten of us make the run with the battering ram, pounding against the thick iron doors a dozen times or more. Yet still they stand. Behind the walls however, mutiny is brewing. The fires have spread, and calls to open the gates can clearly be made out. Yet the English commander holds back, choosing to sacrifice his own rather than suffer the dishonour of surrender. Finally he can hold them no more. The gates open, and like lambs to the slaughter, the English troops rush out into the workyard, coming face to face with the bulk of Sir James's troops.

In a fit of glory we storm the tower, laying down all those in our way as we chase the prize we have been sent to claim. But as the smoke clears and the dust settles, he is nowhere to be found, and instead, nearly twenty of our men lie dead. And once again I must ask, why do we fight? The battle is over, though the war remains unwon. But the tower remains, through storm and siege she still stands. And better still, we have freed it. So, perhaps there is hope for us yet.

# AGE OF CASTLES

### THE CASTLES OF INVERCLYDE

It is a common misconception that Inverclyde had few castles. Indeed at one point there were ten castles scattered throughout the district, although little

*Castle of Easter Greenock*

remains of them today, with Newark being the only one still standing in its original state. The oldest was the Castle of Easter Greenock, which stood in the east end of the town, close to where the Knowe Road runs. There was a castle here from around the mid thirteenth century. The original occupants were the Gailbraith family. One notable member of the family was Hugh de Grenok who swore fealty to Edward Longshanks after the battle of Lanark in 1296. The family were survived through the Crawfords, who remained in occupancy at the castle until the late middle ages. Another early castle in the town stood on the site of the Well Park. The Shaw family acquired the Barony of Wester Greenock through intermarriage with the Galbraiths during the reign of Robert III. The Shaws were for a long time the cup bearers of the Scottish Kings, a fact which is commemorated by the covered cups still visible at the Well park. The castle was rebuilt several times, most famously by John Shaw III who built the Mansion House on the site of the older castle where it remained until it was demolished in 1886 during railway tunnelling. As well as these two, there were also Castles situated at Duchal outside of Kilmacolm, Levan on the Cloch Road, Dunrod near IBM and Ardgowan outside of Inverkip. Many

*The Mansion House*

of these were in existence during the time of Wallace and the Bruce and their tenants surely played their parts in Scotland's battle for independence.

### THE WARS OF INDEPENDENCE

In the summer of 1296, John Balliol, King of Scotland surrendered his crown and along with some fifteen hundred of Scotland's nobles swore fealty to King Edward of England. Balliol, who had the unflattering nickname "Toom Tabard" meaning empty coat, ruled for less than 4 years and was regarded as a somewhat useless King. He was the great-grandson of David, Earl of Huntingdon, who in turn was the grandson of King David 1 of Scotland (1124

- 1153). However his attempts to stand up to the English failed and being unable to unite his people, the war was easily won by England. Scottish nobles owned lands in both Scotland and England, and were divided in their loyalties to such and extent that the sides on which they fought were continually changing. His reign ended in disgrace when he submitted himself as a vassal to a representative of Edward I of England. To show that Scotland was no longer to be an independent kingdom, Edward removed

*Well Park gates and covered cups*

the Stone of Destiny, on which the Scottish kings were crowned, and had it taken to England. All the papers and documents that might prove Scotland's independence were destroyed. Over the next eighteenth months, the English assembled a document, known as "The Ragman Roll" containing all the names of those who submitted to the King Edward. In Renfrewshire, as with elsewhere in the country, many powerful Knights swore fealty to the new King including Hugh de Grenhok and Gilbert fitz Gregoire de Crourtheryk ( Lord of Gourock). All those who swore fealty were allowed to retain their lands and titles, although greater tributes were required by their new master, and English troops were garrisoned in many Scottish castles in order to deter the threat of rebellion. Yet the oath of allegiance was regarded simply as a contract of convenience and many Scottish Lords had no intention of remaining subjects of the English King. Though Edward thought he had subdued Scotland, he was mistaken, for he had not been back in England long when William Wallace stepped into the arena to fight for Scotland.

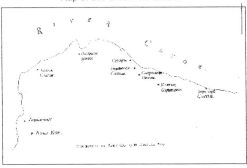
*Map of the Greenock Castles*

## ARDGOWAN

The castle at Ardgowan was one of the many fortresses built during the wars of independence and used to keep the country under subjection. It played a strategically important part in the English occupation of Renfrewshire. After Wallaces victory at the battle of Stirling, King Edward Longshanks was still able to hold control of several key garrisons in Scotland. One of these was Ardgowan at Inverkip, which through its position on the Clyde was the perfect point for landing troops from either England or Ireland. Also, despite being surrounded by Scottish rebel forces, the castle could easily be supplied by the English fleet stationed along the Ayrshire coast. Lying on the edge of the Clyde valley, close to the main route from secure English fortresses in the south, Inverkip became the perfect place from which to stage Edward's campaign to seize control of Renfrewshire. At the head of this operation was an English Knight named Sir John de Soules, a tactician who grasped the significance of Inverkip

*Ardgowan Tor*

in relation to Scottish resistance. The war plan was to see Inverkip taken by forces from the south, where it would be joined by a larger force travelling from the west, thus securing the Forth-Clyde line. However the attempts failed and the English learned that Inverkip could not be supported by forces from the south and it was assigned to the command forces stationed at Roxburgh. Following this, the castle came into the direct hands of English Knights from Essex and Yorkshire. At this time it is believed that a great siege engine was under construction at the Castle, a theory supported by a number of documents relating to the Scottish campaigns. If this is the case it is likely that many of the locals were employed as carpenters and the castle would have played host to a great number of English engineers.

After Wallaces death, Inverkip was used as prison for the Bruces nephew Sir Thomas Randolph, an example of how well guarded the fortress must have been. The last mention of the castle during the wars of independence is made in Barbours poem "The Bruce", when he mentions that the it was "stuffit ful o' Englishmen" during a siege by Scottish forces. At this time, Sir Philip De Mowbray, on the run from the Bruces forces, took refuge in the castle and then escaped by boat. Following the wars of independence, the castle passed into the hands of the Stewart family after King Robert III, descendant of The Bruce, granted lands to his natural son Sir John Stewart. From this time on the castle became the centre of power in the area, and by the end of the eighteenth century, the Stewarts, united with the Shaws through marriage, owned most of the surrounding lands.

# Auld Durrod

# Cold Heart

Dad says the ice on the lake is too thick for fishing; I know different. The fish have been under there a good while; they'll be hungry for some nice fed worms.

I find a good spot at the edge of the frozen water; the edge of the lake drops off sharp, and I'm good and hidden by the trees hanging over my head. Hidden for good reason; these are the lands of the Castle Dunrod, and if any of the Lord Lindsay's men catch me it's not a salmon I'll be carrying home to Mother and Father and Elsbeth tonight.

I slide the knife - my father's gift - from its rabbit skin sheath - my sister's work - smiling a small smile - my mother's smile - at the fact that this little weapon lives in a pouch made from the pelt of its first victim. Then the thought is gone and I'm stabbing at the ice between my feet - feet which sit lightly on the surface, lightly. I like this lake but have no wish for a cold bath in it on this morning.

I was right - the ice is packed hard but it's thin enough, and my good sharp knife makes quick work of it. Before long I have a goodly sized hole, a round door into the dark freezing water beneath. I reach for the pole I have propped against a stump of tree off to my right and, leaning it on my thigh for balance, I fetch Brother Worm from my pocket. Brother Worm was, until a little time ago, rooting happily in the hard earth of the forest at my back. Until I came along to pluck Brother Worm away from his daily life for a higher purpose. Brother Worm will, if all goes well, sacrifice himself to feed a needy family, a selfless act I'm sure the Maker would look kindly upon come the time to blow the horn and call the odds. I say a prayer in to myself that the fattest fish will be hungry this morning and pop Brother Worm under my tongue to keep him placid for a little while.

The rod is barely in my hands when the sound begins; a thrumming of the earth under me, a cracking and splintering of trees and branches which fills the canopy of air between the lake and the sky and seems to come from all around me. Three things happen;

A man, stumbling over his own feet, dishevelled and wild-eyed, his clothes torn and stained by thorns and soil, bursts through the foliage ten feet to my left. He apparently did not expect to exit the woods so abruptly; were the lake not frozen solid over, he would be up to his neck now. As it is, he slides on his belly ten feet before scrambling to a half-run, half-skate along the frozen water.

The second thing is a word. Spoken very softly, almost under someone's breath, it's nevertheless a word I hear clear as day in the cold air; it makes

me wish I were suddenly at home by a pot of soup hanging over a fire. It's a cold voice. Cold.

"Gentlemen," it says.

Simply that.

At this, the third thing happens; the thing I see every time my eyes are closed and old man Night has almost claimed me. The thing I can never remove from my memory.

Twelve white horses - I don't remember counting them, but I know there were twelve, somehow - leap from the forest which circles this hidden lake, landing together, gracefully, fearless of the thin packed ice. Twelve mighty animals shooting steam-breath from their long noses, supporting black, hooded riders - but I can see no white plumes of frost-breath coming from those dark holes where faces should be.

None at all.

I'm as frozen as the lake for the next few minutes; helpless to watch this scene unfold before me. Dimly I realise that in my shock I have swallowed Brother Worm whole; there's a few old wives' tales broken. Still, his worries are long forgotten as I watch from my shadowy nook under the hanging oak branches; I watch the dark riders advance slowly on their hapless prey; I watch the poor shambling folly of a man, breathless on his hands and knees on the ice, apparently unmindful of the frost which surely eats into his palms; I watch his expression change from weary resignation to rabid terror as the dozen steeds, their coats almost disappearing against the winter sky, stop as one, forming a circle around their victim twenty feet wide.

I watch - I cannot help but watch - as the cowled figure of Alexander Lindsay de Dunrod steps out onto the lake, a small smile flickering on his lips, and walks on, his feet steady as if walking on packed earth, walks on, toward the huddled mass of a man in the centre of the frozen water.

"Crawford," he says, and this one word chills me, makes me want to break my cover and run for home, yet I cannot, my eyes fixed to this spectacle. Dunrod slides back the charcoal hood of his cloak, to reveal his high-cheekboned face, haughty and aloof. The Lord Dunrod. Owner and laird of these lands. The man I must rightly fear when I fish this water.

"Crawford, Crawford, Crawford," Dunrod says wearily, shaking his head as if speaking to an ignorant child, crouching down on his haunches to look into the man's frightened eyes. Crawford - I can only assume now that this is the man's name - whimpers softly, sniffling and making soft noises which might be prayer or curse.

"What am I to do with a man such as you, Crawford?" Dunrod's icy voice carries out over the ice toward me, and I think I hear a tinge of anger in it now, a righteous indignation. I think Crawford opens his mouth to speak

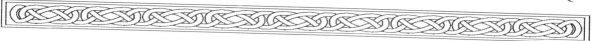

- to offer some kind of penance to this dark priest - but Dunrod carries on regardless. "I'll tell you what I'm to do, shall I?"

He stands, placing his hands on the small of his back and staring at the sky for a moment, talking to the heavens instead of the man at his feet. "You like the fish in my waters so very much. I'll give you all you might need. Gentlemen."

That simple word again - yet a shudder works its way over me nonetheless, and I look on as Dunrod's twelve companions draw small glinting daggers from their robes, holding them by their ears for a moment before hurling them into the centre of their equine circle - at Crawford, I naturally think. But no; the blades hit the ice with a soft sharp noise, making a smaller circle around the helpless man, now a weeping heap far from his senses.

I look on, cursed observer, as a dark crack moves off from each dagger-point towards Crawford, moving closer and closer, moving under what I would swear were their own steam, widening, until they reach Crawford, twelve wide paths in the ice which meet under this poor soul, and he only has time to utter a strangled cry before the dark chilling waters take him as their own.

There is silence for a moment - the riders, the horses, the black figure of Dunrod, all stock still as if painted against the sky - and then Dunrod, Lord Dunrod, lifts his head a little, and says in a playful way, "I've not killed a man in a fit of pique since last summer." He utters a mirthless little laugh and turns to head back the way he came.

But not before turning to me.

Not before smiling.

Not before winking.

I rise from my fishing hole then; then I move, then I run, run home, and I'll never stop.

I'll never stop.

## The Vision Of Auld Dunrod
## At The Bogle Stane

Auld Dunrod was a warlock guide
Wha wonned by the clyde
He sleepit on the Bogle Stane
And there this vision spied

He lookit our the loch o' Clyde
A sicht o' glamourie
For forests wide o' firren trees
Cam doun close to the sea

And whiles in opening o' the noo
A claw's abode he saw
A' ser about wi paliades
That stood up in a raw

The hovels were o' wattles made
An were chokefu o' reek
Lasses were liltin at the quern
A' browned wi the sweek

But what is yon at Kempock point
Canoes glide twa or three
A'hewd wi stonen axe, and fire
Out of a gude fir tree

An in them naked sauaes
He counted dozens twa,
Wi' wild beasts scored ther skin
The queerest ere he saw

Good blades had they, blunt at the end
That were baith sharp an' sheen
An spears that rattled when they flew
An bows an' arrows keen.

They paidled up an down the firth
Ilk man his own canoe
For naething then but boats o tree
Were on clydes waters blue

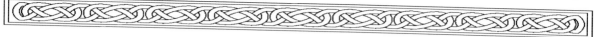

When lo! owr Gourock point he saw
A sicht o' meikle pride;
There were twenty Roman ships an three
Cam rowin up the clyde

Fill'd the sails were wi the wind,
The  oarsmen plied the car;
An' tenty the mid channel kept,
An' shunn'd the banky shore

A' round about the galleys sides
The shields hung in a raw,
The mariners wi wonder gazed
On the heich hills they saw

An some row'd up, an farrer up
Until Dunglass they gain,
Aboon the great Rock of the Clyde
That tow'rs above the plain

There an the shore the camp was built,
For there the legions lay;
An Julius the rampart reard
To keep the clansat bay

Then mariners and soldiers
They mingled on the shore;
These told of mountains, these of sea
And Isles ne'er seen before

Then camp an galleys vanished
Before that warlock's e'en
An lo! before his wond'ring gaze
Appears a peaceful scene

Still as of yare the sea loch fills
The hollow of the hills:
Still ebbeth when the ocean ebbs
And when that flows it fills

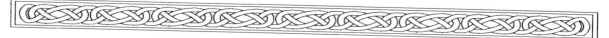

Stil branching lochs afar ascend
Among the mountains high;
An' still that Rock of Clyde stands fast,
While rolls the river by

But changed the scene from what it was
Two thousand years ago;
Nor tree canoe the river bears,
Nor presence of a foe

But iron vessels to and fro
On varied pathways glide;
Some driv'n by wind, an some by steam
Right gallantly they glide

For Broomielaw those hold their course
Ascending 'gainst the stream
For Erin, or the Hudson those
Or the West Highlands steam

The Warlock sees the glassy firth
A gay wi sails an boats.
Yachts, schooners, tugs, brigs an ships
A' kind o' thing that floats

He sees the Gareloch windin' up
Wi villas on its side;
An' Helenburghs snawy cots
Uprising frae the tid

The flow'ry fields o' Cardross fair
Appear'd before his e'en;
Dumbartons toun , Dumbartons rock
Beside the waves are seen

Kilpatricks hills, wi rugged braes
A glimpse  of Leven side
An far awa Ben Lomond's peaks
With streaks of snow are spied

Then thronging Greenock he beheld
Port Glasgow on the brae
An' high Argyles magnificence
Of mountains far away

A fairy picture sure did then
Before that wizard shine
When hark an engine shakes the earth
And thunders down the line

The puffing smoke, the flying wheels
An the air shaking sound
Awakened that wizard hoar
Out of his seers stound.

The ferlies which he saw that day
He had nae words to say ;
He waukened an' he only heard
Winds whistlin' on the brae

An' the whaups pipin' on the bent
An' beetles drowsy drone
An' muir cocks wi' their bic, bic, bir
Upon the moorland  lone

Syne he to Kilmacolm sweet  vale
Has ta en his homeward way
But never till he de'ed fogat
The ferlies o' that day.


30 Verses - as quoted in
*Much About Kilmalcolm, Alexander 1872;*
Claimed by Charles to date
back to the time of Dunrod

The following letter and journal fragments have been transcribed and reprinted with the kind permission of the Macintosh family archive.

Dear Macintosh

My most sincere apologies for the time it has taken for you to finally receive the enclosed items. While I am sure you more than anyone can appreciate the legal wranglings these kind of situations can cause, this will have done little to ease your mind. These then are the pages from the journal of Mr Malcolm Doyle, and with them, the ring given him by your daughter Elizabeth.

The journal pages and related personal effects belonging to Mr Doyle were found by William Allen in the grounds of the Dunrod estate. The pages were bound together by the ring and this, tied to a rock. It is my understanding that there is currently some dispute over ownership of the land and this certainly slowed down the process of forwarding these items to yourself. In my opinion, Allen was also trespassing and more than likely poaching when he found the pages, and his reluctance to pinpoint the precise location of the find made determining ownership of the items a most lamentable business.

Clearly however, it is to yourself and your poor daughter that these remnants belong, the last fragment in particular appears to be not so much a journal entry as a letter addressed directly to her. I would caution you however, to think carefully before allowing Elizabeth to read these pieces, in my opinion they are not suitable for the delicate female constitution.

I had a man sent down to Inverkip to collect the items, and while there, he asked after Alexander Lindsay, with particular reference to the events reported in Mr Doyle's journal. Of late Lindsay has not been seen at his castle or the surrounding grounds, he is apparently travelling in the east. However, I am sad to report that Lindsay does indeed have a name for himself as a dabbler in the black arts and has for a goodly number of years terrorised this little village. It seems then, unlikely that we shall see Mr Doyle return, and must hope that whatever sinister fate befell him, he has since passed on into the protection of our Lord, where no such evil spirit may again cause him harm.

My thoughts are with you and with Elizabeth.

Peace be with you.

Your friend

John Harkins

"Having arrived from Ayrshire, I have stopped at Inverkip. I could easily have travelled through the evening to reach Greenock and from there find passage home, but I was famished and for once, fancied myself more firm lodgings than aboard ship. The inn is pleasant enough and not for nothing does the kitchen comes well recommended. What a feast!

After my meal, I sat for a little while in the company of some local characters who were keen to impress me with tales and songs. As the night drew on, the conversation grew darker, and I was told in very serious tones of the exploits of one Alexander Lindsay, a landowner hereabouts. It seems that this man, has fallen into the service of Satan himself, and has been bringing these dark forces to bear on his tenants and those who labour in the surrounding fields. His foul temperament seeks to spoil the crops and the cattle of the other landowners by means of a sinister magick. It is said also that he has a number of witches in his service. Here the conversation grew still more hushed, as it seems that many of these familiars live within the village of Inverkip itself! Also, on several occasions early in the morning, Lindsay has been spied in the fields, piercing the skin of cows to draw blood for arcane purpose.

I eventually excused myself and retired to bed, having enjoyed both a good meal and a good yarn, I slept well. It was my intent to rise early, but I have slept til the midmorning, and so I will simply walk to Greenock by the Largs road. With luck I will find passage in the evening, if not then I will stay in The White Hart, as one more day's delay will make little difference."

"What turns fate takes! I left Inverkip in good humour and weather and headed up onto the moorland path. I had been walking for a little over an hour when the sky blackened. Shortly thereafter the mist rolled down from the hills. I stopped then, so as not wander from the path. However when the mist finally lifted, then came the rains. And what rains! I have passed down Greenock way a number of times now, and there was never such a place for the four seasons in a day. Sodden and not a little disheartened by the storm, I was set to turn back for Inverkip there to spend another pleasant evening by the Inn hearth, However, I could see in the near distance the castle which could only belong to Alexander Lindsay. Stories by the fireside of an evening are all well and good, but in the midst of a hellish afternoon storm, I had little reservation in approaching the castle. I would admit however, to firmly grasping my crucifix as I knocked upon the huge oaken door.

A tall, slender man opened the door, this transpired to be Lindsay himself, no servants seemed to be in attendance. I explained my plight and he welcomed me in without hesitation as, he told me "You never turn away a

stranger in a storm". This did not seem to me to be the fiend described by the fellows at the inn and it occurred to me that they were perhaps having a little fun at my expense.

Lindsay showed me to a room at the top of the West Wing. There is a small window which overlooks the distant hills.

I will stay here for the evening and take my leave in the morning."

"This has been a most curious day. After a marvellous evening meal provided by my host I retired to bed. I did not wake until the late afternoon! I hurried to get washed and dressed, hoping to leave immediately for Greenock for the evening sailings. I could not find my host to offer him my thanks, so instead wrote him a short letter, leaving him my address that we might correspond at some later date. However, I found the front door to be locked, with no key to be seen. I once more looked for my host, calling loudly for him by name, again to no avail. Regrettably, all of the windows on the lower floor of the castle are too small to scramble through and so currently I find myself locked in the castle, alone. It will be dusk soon, and Lindsay has not yet returned."

"I have passed the remainder of the afternoon reading from a copy of The Iliad I found in Lindsay's library. There were a great many interesting books to be found there, but most were written in languages I could not understand. I also noted a number of books which did appear to contain sinister diagrams and magickal text such as would add weight to the allegations of the Inverkip villagers. Having been not a little unsettled by this, I find myself starting at the merest sound. And what sounds there have been echoing round these halls, empty but for myself. Strange whistlings and murmurings, a shrieking or screaming which sounds terrifying and real, yet so very far away. On two occasions, I have nearly leapt from my seat upon hearing a whisper at my ear, only to turn and find no one there. The reading has kept my mind at rest for a time, but with night now falling I can think of little else but the many rooms in the castle, and the many evil spirits I fear dwell within."

"It is but a short time later. I have been staring from my window out across the way, hoping to catch a glimpse of someone passing. And sure enough, a shape emerged. A little cowled figure, wandering not along the path, but down from the hills. The figure was too small to be Lindsay, but did seem to be coming towards the castle in a laborious but determined fashion. I waited til this person had come closer, and waved from the window to try and attract their attention. And at once they glanced upward. I could see now it was an elderly woman, hunched over but most certainly

not frail. She had clearly seen me, yet chose to ignore me and walked around the castle in order that she was out of view to me. Disturbed still further, I sat silently for an age, listening, hoping to hear if she entered. Apparently she did not."

"It is a little before eight o'clock, a short while ago, Lindsay brought some food up to my room. He apologised for his disappearance earlier in the day, explaining that he had been running some very important errands. The door had been locked he said, because he does not trust the labourers or villagers. This I suppose, is possible, however, I sat by my window, watching the path leading up to the doorway, and listening, all evening listening, for the slightest sound, and I neither saw nor heard Lindsay arrive back at Castle. I thanked him for his hospitality, and made to be on my way. Lindsay however, was having none of it, insisting that the least he could offer me after such a day was another evenings lodgings. While I was keen to be away, the rain was once again lashing down, and my half hearted attempts to explain my departure were beginning to look most ingracious. I agreed therefore to stay one final night.
I asked him then about the woman I had saw come by, and he told me that she too was a guest of his this evening, an old acquaintance of the family down visiting from Lochwinnoch. He told me that one more guest was to arrive, a man of holy orders. I must admit that this did put me more at my ease. Yet here Lindsay grew very sombre, asking that for the duration of the evening I should remain in my room, as he and his guests had "a serious business" to attend to.
In all honesty, I was not overkeen to spend the night in his company, and so will instead settle down with The Iliad."

"Dearest Elizabeth,
As I write, my crucifix sits upon the table just in front of me. I now fear for my life, and my soul. I wish that I was with you now.
Downstairs I can hear them chanting still, and as they sing, so too do the restless spirits that rattle round these walls. There is a bad magick at work here, and I have watched them prepare.
A short time ago, as I sat reading by my little window, I saw a carriage draw up by the front of the castle, and a robed man emerged and drifted indoors. This was the monk my host had spoken of earlier. The carriage trundled off into the night and I returned to my book.
Not long after this, I heard a great deal of commotion downstairs and although my host had stated that I should remain in my room, curiosity got the better of me. I stepped quietly from my room, and peered down from the stairwell to the great hall below. And here were Lindsay, the old

woman and the monk, arguing loudly. I could not understand what they were arguing about, but Lindsay kept shaking his head and gesturing to a chain he was wearing around his neck. There seemed to be some kind of ornamental piece upon the end of it, but I could not rightly make it out. Eventually, the argument quelled, and the three busied themselves by leafing through some of the volumes I had noted earlier in the library. Ever and again, they would stop to cast something across the open floor. I knew Elizabeth, that this was evil at work, that I should not linger, yet I sat transfixed. I watched as they drew strange shapes and symbols upon the stone floor, and here the chanting started. The temperature dropped considerably, and thankfully this seemed to rouse me. I resolved to watch no more, but I had not decided upon my course of action until I heard all three of them calling out to the Devil. They listed his many names, and I could listen no longer.

This is a damned place, and I must leave before I am taken, therefore Elizabeth, it is my intent to clamber from this window down to the moors below.

The weather however is against me, and so in case I should fail in this venture, I would not have you imagine it is you I have run from. I will roll these last pages together, and loop them with the silver band you have given me. I have chipped out a little stone from the walls and I will bind the ring and pages to this. I shall throw this from my window out toward the wall by the road where I might easily retrieve it. You would know Elizabeth, that I would not willingly be separated from that ring, so should it come back into your possession, it is because I have failed in my efforts to leave this place. I pray that you need never read these pages.

All my love always."

# The Ballad Of Auld Dunrod

Auld Dunrod was a gowstie carl,
As ever ye micht see;
And gin he wisna' a warlock wicht,
There was nane in the haill countrie.

Auld Dunrod he stack a pin -
A boutrie pin - in the wa',
And when he wanted his neighbour's milk
He just gaed the pin a thraw.

He milkit the Laird o' Kellies kye,
And a' the kye o' Dunoon;
And auld Dunrod gat far mair milk
Than wad mak' a gabbert swim.

The cheese he made were numerous,
And wonerous to descry
For the kyth't as gin they had been grule
Or peats set up to dry.

And there was nae cumerauld man about
Wha cam' to him for skill,
That gif he dadna dae him guid,
He didna dae him ill.

But the kirk got word o' Dunrod's tricks,
And the Session they took him hand;
And naething was left but auld Dunrod
Forsooth maun leave the land.

Sae auld Dunrod he muntit his stick -
His broomstick muntit he -
And he flychter't twa'r three times aboot,
And syne through the air did flee.

And he flew awa' by auld Greenock tower,
And by the Newark ha'.
Ye wadna kent him in his flicht
Be a buddock or a craw.

And he flew to the Rest and be Thankfu' Stane -
A merry auld carle was he;
He stottit and fluffer't as he had been wud.
Or drucken wi' the barley bree.

But a rountree grew at the stane -
It is there unto this day,
And gin ye dinna find it still,
Set doun that it's away.

And he ne'er wist o' the rountree
Till he cam dunt thereon;
His magic broomstick tint its spell,
And he daudit on the stone.

His heid was hard, and the Stane was sae,
And whan they met ane anither,
It was hard to say what wad be the weird
Of either the tane or the tither.

But the Stane was muilt like a lampet shell,
And sae was Auld Dunrod;
When ye munt a broomstick to tak a flicht,
Ye had best tak anither road.

The neighbours gathert to see the sicht,
The Stane's remains they saw;
But as for Auld Dunrod himsel',
He was carriet clean awa'.

And monie noy't, as weill they micht,
The Rest and be Thankfu' Stane;
And ilk ane said it had been better far,
Gin Dunrod had staid at hame.

And what becam o' Auld Dunrod
Was doubtfu' for to say,
Some said he wasna there ava,
But flew anither way.

# Last Orders Please

The rain lashed down heavy as Alexander reached the door of the Cock & Bull Inn. It was late, but thankfully there was still a light in the window. The warm air clashed against his sodden clothes as he stepped inside, sending a shiver down his hunched spine. He was getting too old for this. Far too old.

He looked around the small Inn, which was nothing more than a glorified sitting room. In the centre of the berth stood two long tables, and beyond them a modest fire place with two chairs, one at either side of a roaring blaze. A damp smell hovered in the air, and what few customers remained took little notice of his arrival. Not quite up to the standards he was once used to, but he was starting to sober up so it would have to do.

Stumbling across the room he arrived at the bar and was greeted by a middle aged woman in a filthy apron who flashed him a toothless grin.

"You're just in time. It's last orders. What can I get you?"

Alexander took a moment to compose himself, shaking of the rain and straightening his hair in an attempt to look slightly less drunk than he was.

"I will have a bottle of you finest whiskey please."

The woman glanced at him suspiciously, and was met with what Alexander believed was a charming and sophisticated grin, but what in fact appeared like a pathetic attempt to convince the barmaid he could afford to pay for the drink. She reached under the bar and placed a dusty bottle on the bar.

"Are you sure you can pay for this?" she asked.

Alexander looked deeply into her eyes, waving his hands maniacally in the air around him.

"No, no. You don't need any money. Instead when I clap my hands three times you will give me the bottle for free."

Clap. Clap. Clap.

The woman just stared at him blankly.

"I'll be needing to see some money before I let you have this."

"That never works anymore." muttered Alexander as he reached into his pocket and pulled out a small handful of coins, peering closely at them and looking slightly disappointed.

"On second thoughts" he said. "You better make it your cheapest bottle."

The fire flickered. The room emptied.

"...and another time, I dropped his man down a hole. Right down. He had it coming though, they all had it coming....Hey, hey you?"

Alexander prodded the man sitting in the opposite chair. But it was no good, he had fallen asleep about an hour ago, right about the point where Alexander started talking about the time he had the De'il over for tea.  He sighed. No one listened anymore.

"Right." shouted the barmaid. "Your times up. Better start making tracks."

"Yes you're probably right." said the old man. And then a flicker of panic crossed his face. "But where will I go?"

"Ain't you got no home to go to?"

Alexander seemed to ponder this question for a moment, and then in a quiet voice, his face blemished by saddness he answered.
"No."
"Well you can't stay here. We're full. Speak to the farmer up the road. Sometimes he lets travellers sleep in his barn."
The old man nodded and then pouring what was left in his companions glass into the whiskey bottle, he wrapped himself in his newly dried cloak and staggered out the door back into the night.
Stumbling along the country road, Alexander had never felt more tired in his life. It wasn't much of a walk, but by the time he reached the gate to the farmyard, the old man wanted nothing more than to lie down and go to sleep. A sheep stood in the yard, eyeing Alexander unhappily, and bleating at him as he approached the farmhouse door.
"Goat." whispered Alexander, waving a hand at the animal. And in a puff the sheep turned into a goat.
"See" he muttered. "I've still got it."
He knocked the door and waited. After a few moments a middle aged man appeared with a lantern.
"Who is it? What d'ye want at this hour?"
"I was just wondering if I could..." began Alexander.
"Holy Mother. Is that you Lord Lindsay. Aye sure it is."
Sobring slightly at the use of his former title, Alexander stared at the man, a smile creeping across his face.
"Do I know you?"
"For sure you do, Lord Lindsay. I'm William Allen. I used to work for you."
"Of course. William Allen. How are you boy?" Alexander had never seen this man in his life, or at least if he had, he certainly didn't remember.
"Fine fine. Would you be looking for somewhere to sleep?" asked William. The old man gave an embarrassed nod.
"I'd take ye in the house, but we haven't the room. There's the barn. Its dry and warmer than a ditch."

William led Alexander by torch light, round through the muddy field to a rickety old barn, and handed him a thin tartan blanket. The old man smiled at the farmer;
"Thank you William."
And with that Alexander made his way into the barn to settle down for a much needed sleep. He took a bale of hay in the corner for a bed. Yes, he thought, this will do nicely. Just sleep. Sleep and rest. But just for a while. Just for a while.
The next morning, William arrived bright and early in the barn. And there sure enough was Lord Lindsay himself, just where he'd left him. Yet as he went to shake the old man awake he was cold to the touch. All the life had went out of him, and what little remained of his soul must have left him in the night, for Auld Dunrod, scourge of the west, was stone dead.
Never mind, thought William, I never liked him anyway.

# Auld Dunrod

"The Lindsays of Dunrod, a wild and warlock race, flourished for centuries in power and affluence and their history is a dark and stormy one."
- Lives of the Lindsays

### Dominus de Dunrod - The House of Dunrod

The Lindsays were an Angus clan, said to be descended from the uplanders and, while there are many important branches of the family, most notably that of Edzel and Balcarres, here we are primarily concerned with those in residence at Dunrod, near Inverkip.

The Lindsays of Dunrod took their name from Dunrod Hill, the impressive summit which lies directly behind Cornalees Bridge Centre. The family were

*The Dunrod Family Seal*

directly descended from Sir James Lindsay, Robert the Bruce's accomplice in the murder of Red Cumyn, and it was James' successor, John Lindsay, who obtained the baronies of Kilbride and Dunrod from Robert II in recognition for the family's loyalty during the Wars of Independence.

The family remained influential in Scotland for many years, intermarrying with the families of Eglinton, Semple and Elphistone, growing into one of the most powerful landowners in the country.

### Auld Dunrod

In the late 16th century, Alexander Lindsay succeeded the family's lands of Dunrod and Kilbride. For twenty years, Alexander enjoyed the trappings of a wealthy man, dwelling in splendour and going nowhere without being accompanied by a troop of twelve attendants on pure white horses. One story speaks of Dunrod's arrogance and indolence: A man named Crawford had committed some wrong against the landowner, and Dunrod had the man sent out onto the middle of a frozen pond, where a hole was cut around him. Crawford dropped into the icy water and perished, and from this day forward, the spot of his death is known as Crawford's Hole.

Apparently, along with his affluence, Dunrod had inherited his family's involvement in an age-old feud between the Cunninghams, the Montgomeries and the Maxwells. The feud stemmed from the that fact that, in 1366, Hugh Eglinton was appointed to the office of Bailey of the Barony of Cunningham. However, his office was contested by the Cunninghams. The feud had continued in many forms until the year 1528, when the Cunninghams had attacked the manor house of the Eglintons,

*Dunrod Hill*

who were allies of the Lindsays and the Montgomeries of Skelmorlie. This brought many more of the powerful families of Renfrewshire into what had been a private battle.

These matters came to a head in 1584, when Montgomerie attacked and killed Maxwell of Stanley, and in return the Maxwell ambushed and killed Montgomerie and his son. Dunrod's personal revenge for this crime is best recounted in Crawford's famous 'History of Renfrewshire':

"....Alexander of Dunrod, having some way or another become engaged in that dreadful and long lasting feud between the Cunninghams and the Montgomeries, killed out of the window of a farmhouse of his own, at Hayton hill, near Glasgow, Alexander Leckie of that Ilk, who was brother in law to Patrick Maxwell of Newark, a great hero and a very bloody man on the side of the Cunninghams."

Up until this time, Dunrod had been spending a great deal of time away from the family estates in Inverkip; however, after the murder of Leckie, he returned to the family home.

It has been stated that Dunrod's subsequent problems were a kind of divine retribution; God's revenge on a murderer. All that can be said is, for earthly reasons or otherwise, the next twenty years saw Dunrod's personal fortune dwindle and his lands shrink. It was during this time that Dunrod turned to the black arts.

It was rumoured that Dunrod became involved with witches living on his remaining lands in Inverkip, gathering with them at Dunrod's Seat, located on the slope of Dunrod Hill. Further rumours suggested that he entertained the Devil himself at his castle.

It is worth noting the possibility that Dunrod had inherited his connections to the practice of witchcraft from the Lindsays; it is now thought in some circles that members of the nobility at that time were involved in a highly organised cult which they used for their own means.

The image of Dunrod as a dark and powerful Warlock is a far cry from the man he was at the end of his life; he was a penniless hermit, his lands having been seized by the Kirk in recompense for his evil deeds, selling charms and potions to any who would entertain him.

Dunrod died soon after in a barn on his former lands in East Kilbride.

### THE DUNROD LEGACY
"Peace has a bower by still Chriswell,
But dark Dunrod conceals a witchcraft spell."

Very little remains today of the infamous Castle Dunrod. Some large stones, standing at the bottom of a gorge by the road to Shielhill; a poor legacy to a family with a powerful, if shadowy, past.

However, Dunrod is remembered in another way, being one of the most infamous characters in Inverclyde's history. As recently as a century ago, parents enforced children's' bedtimes with the chilling promise that 'Auld Dunrod' would get them. Thus, this larger than life character has become woven irrevocably into the folklore of the area, celebrated in numerous tales passed from generation to generation, and most famously in two anonymous poems commemorating his dark deeds. This book marks the first occasion

*The Bogle Stone*

the two poems, 'The Ballad of Auld Dunrod' and 'The Vision of Auld Dunrod,' have ever been published in a single volume.

The first of these is thought not to have been written down until more than a century after Dunrod's death, and was probably composed while Dunrod was extant. Presented in its fullest original form, the poem chronicles his black deeds, and ends rather cryptically with Dunrod flying on his broomstick to the Bogle Stone; this, in turn, gave rise to the second poem.

This second piece was composed a good many years later than its companion, and gives an account of a mystical vision Dunrod experienced at the Bogle Stone, concerning Inverclyde's past, present and future.

The Bogle Stone itself has long been associated with strange occurrences, and earned the local parish a skeptical and superstitious
reputation. In the nineteenth century, a minister attempted to destroy the stone using explosives, succeeding only in shattering it. Superstition subsequently came into play, and the stone was fitted back together, and an inscription attached:

'I am the far-famed Bogle Stane
By worldly priest abhorr'd
But now I am myself again
By Auchenleck restored.'

The stone still stands in Port Glasgow, a memory to the ghost who, it is said, haunts the stone still. And who knows - perhaps the 'Bogle' is the spectre of Dunrod himself, continuing his evil legacy into a new age.

### Old Scots dialect used in "The Ballad of Auld Dunrod"

| | |
|---|---|
| goustie | ghostly, unearthly |
| boutrie | of the elder tree |
| Laird o Kellie | Bannatyne, the Laird of Kellie in Innerkip Parish |
| soum | make a lighter swim |
| grule | appeared as if they had, like moss, been baked in the sun |
| flychterit | fluttered |
| huddock | from a carrion crow |
| wud | bounded and whisked about |
| barley bree | ale |
| rountree | mountain ash |
| daudit | fell violently down |
| muilt | crushed |
| noy't | blamed |
| ava | at all |

# DANCE WITH THE DE'IL

In the days of superstition and religious fervour, cries of witchcraft
echo around a tiny village and a young girl is forced to face her demons...

It happened not too far from here, but so long ago that few can even
remember her name. "They burned a witch in Inverkip", they say. Or so
they say. And a sad tale it is too, but one which starts, as many do, in joy
and jubilation. For Mary Lamont was a welcomed child, a blessing to her
parents who had waited so long for a baby. And so when she finally arrived
on the first day of August in the year 1644, there was much celebration in
the little village of Innerkip. The people there were simple God-fearing
folk, who kept one ear out for the church bell, and the other for the clip-
clop of the devil's hooves. And so Mary was quick to be brought to the
church and baptised, her parents choosing Jean Scott to be her Godmother,
for she was said to be good and pious and had long been a friend of the
family.  In the church on that sunny autumn day the reverend blessed the
child, and asked of Jean:
"Will thou watch over this child? Keep her course straight and far from the
rocks? Teach her to use the gifts with which she has been blessed?"
"I shall," answered Jean.
And so they left the church that day, believing the devil to be far from
their door.
The years passed quick, and Mary  grew even quicker. She was a happy
child, always smiling and laughing, taking great pleasure from life, and in
turn giving it to all who were ever around her. Her days were spent in joy,
playing with the other children of the village in the Daff Glen. And every
day as she left the cottage, her mother would remind her;
"Never stray from the path Mary, no matter how tempting it might be."
Jean too spent many hours with her, spinning her tales of Kings and Queens
and of far off lands and magical creatures, teaching her the secrets of
nature; which plants cured the most common ills, where the purest water
flowed and how to milk the kye. Mary would accompany her when she
went to tend the sick of the village, and  often they would go walking
together in the hills and the heather, far from the little village by the river.
Jean treated her like the daughter she could never have, and loved her
very much.
Then one day, a short while after her fifth birthday, Mary noticed strange
things happening in the village. Her mother would not let her call on Jean,
claiming she was too ill for visitors. But that day as she played in the Daff
Glen, she heard one boy whisper;
"My mother says the De'ils loose in Innerkip, and Jean Scott danced wi'
him."
Mary began crying when she heard this, though she did not quite know

what the boy meant. And so she ran home and asked her mother, who said:

"Do not listen to such gossip Mary. Only fools who know no better say such things."

And she told Mary that she was to stay indoors from now on, in case she got sick like Jean.

But then a few days later, a black carriage rode into the village, with four horses to draw it. The children chased behind as it rode towards the church house, where men with hats tall and black, and books thick with learning descended, setting tongues wagging and the church bell ringing.

The next morning, Mary watched from her bedroom window as the men of the village dragged Jean from her home, and marched her to the church house. They did the same with Janet Patterson and Janet Loudon, all the time crying "Burn the Witch. Burn the Witch."

That afternoon, a great crowd had gathered in the village square, and Mary's mother and father had both gone to find out what had happened to Jean, leaving their daughter free to sneak out of the house after them. The streets were lined with people, who had come from far and wide; farmers from Greenock and fishermen from Gourock. "Burn the Witch. Burn the Witch," they cried. It was all too much for the little girl, and she got such a fright as she felt a hand suddenly slap down on her shoulder. She gazed up and saw a handsome man in a top hat new. What a pity she did not see the bright red tail he had to match. He craned down, and grinned a mouthful of sharp white teeth, his eyes flashing red. And in a voice thick and slow as treacle he spoke:

"Hello. What is your name?"

But Mary didn't reply, and instead stood icy still, frozen with fright.

"Cat got your tongue?"

Mary shook her head. The gentleman nodded knowingly, patting the little girl on the head as he stood up straight.

"Mary." The little girl turned to see her Mother looking down at her scornfully. "Did I not tell you to remain indoors?"

The gentleman turned to Mary's mother and said:

"A pretty daughter you have. You must take care that she does not lose her way."

And with that he trotted back into the crowd, quickly disappearing from sight.

The little girl, still shivering with fright turned round, and gazed up at her mother, hugging her leg tightly as the two set off for the village square.

The sight which befell little Mary that day made her light soul heavy. For when they reached the village square, there was Jean, and those others accused, strapped to wooden stakes, the villagers advancing on them

with burning torches. "Burn the witch. Burn the witch," they cried. And looking on, the men of authority stood, their silence seeming to sanction the violence, and the cries grew louder. "Burn the witch. Burn the witch." But then a strange hush fell over the crowd, and in a loud clear voice, one of the men addressed the three women;

"Confess to that of which you have been accused, and you shall be spared death by fire. Instead you three shall suffer excommunication only, and shall leave this place forthwith. Janet Loudoun, does thou confess?"

The women looked up weakly, struggling with the words.

"Aye."

The man nodded sagely.

"Janet Patterson, does thou confess?"

"Aye."

Again the man nodded, and turning lastly to Jean, he asked:

"Jean Scott, does thou confess?"

Jean looked up at the crowd, smiling at Mary, who could do nothing but stare on in terror. And then in a clear voice, she said:

"'Tis all the same, to be called a witch as to be counted one. So I shall confess and live in shame, rather than die in it."

And so they were cut down and that day, Jean Scott left Innerkip, never to return. Mary never spoke to her again, but she could not forget the events of that day, or the fear that they had placed in her heart.

That winter, her mother was much troubled by whisperings in the village about her friendship with Jean and the time her daughter had spent with her. They longed to cry witch, and if the De'il was anywhere in Innerkip in those days, he was on the tongues of the gossips who seemed to prey on the weak. Always under the eye of suspicion, Mary's mother took ill with worry, and before the year was out, she was in her grave. Mary did not quite understand, and took little from the fact that her mother was in heaven. The young girl's father's heart was crushed, and he spoke few words to his daughter after that day.

And so as the years passed, Mary became a solitary girl, a dreamer who spent her days among the hills and the heather, wishing for a happier life. She was surely the loneliest soul for miles around and of all the girls among the parish, their was only one whom she could count as a friend, Katherine Scott, a kinswoman of Jean, from Murdiestoun. Katie was older than Mary, but would sometimes accompany her on long walks, trying hard to lighten her soul with talk of far off places and dreams for the future. And then one day as the two wandered in the hills above the ruined castle of Auld Dunrod, him that had done such bad deeds not fifty years past, Katie turned to Mary and asked.

"Tell me Mary, what sort of dreams hath you?"

She paused slightly, her voice struggling to get the words out.
"Of late, Kettie, ought but nightmares."
Katie smiled sweetly at her young friend.
"Ach Mary, y'have such a heavy heart. It is your thirteenth birthday on the morrow, is it not?"
Mary nodded.
"Aye. It is."
"Well then," said Katie "I have a surprise for you."
At this Mary's eyes lit up and she asked excitedly:
"What is it Katie, what is my surprise?"
"Come to the Daff Glen this night, after the candles are out. Then you shall have it."
And so that night, when a calm hush had fallen over the little village, Mary sneaked from her house and quietly through the streets she passed, the autumn leaves blowing at her back, sending a cold chill down her spine. Up the dark path she made her way, into the glen, the wind rustling in the trees. Onwards she walked, for such a time as she thought she might be lost. And then she caught a glimpse of a fire through the trees. In the midst of a clearing, it stood, and around it danced Marget McKenzie, Janet Scot and Katie. And there were others with them too, strangers shrouded in hooded robes. Mary became frightened at the sight of it all, and was about to turn back when she heard Katie call out to her.
"Mary." They had stopped dancing now. "Mary, come and join us."
And so the young girl edged nervously into the clearing, beckoned onwards by Katie, and a strange desire to know more.
"What is all this? Why are ye dancing in the forest?" whispered Mary.
"This is our coven." Announced Katie, with great pride. And at this, Mary turned pale white.
"Oh no Kettie, witching is wrong. D'yea no remember what happened to Jeanie?"
Katie looked solemnly at Mary, her eyes dark and full of fire.
"Aye. I do. And I remember what they said of her. But don't you ever want more Mary? Don't you want pretty things and a happy life? Don't you deserve them?" And  then she stretched out her hand, and said;
"We can help you Mary. We can make you happy"
Mary looked back towards the dark path, and then at the warm inviting glow of the clearing. She would be safe here, she thought. She would belong. And at that, she took Katie's hand.
Oh what sorrow. For Mary was already dancing with the De'il. She just couldn't see him.
Katie wasted no time in training Mary in the ways of witchcraft. And just as she had been with Jean, Mary was always quick to learn. Oh it is sad to

tell, how quickly Mary let her soul go dark, and sadder still to speak of her deeds. Of misty mornings, the two would wander out across the fields among the kye. And there they would draw an old rag over the mouth of a mug, and say:

"In Gods name, God send us milk, God send it and meikkle of it."

And in doing so, Mary and Katie could steal their neighbours milk, and use it to make butter, or cheese. This trick she was glad to know, for Mary and her father were very poor.  And thus the young witch also used her new-found knowledge to gain employment as a servant girl at a big farmhouse in Gourock. And on the days when her master had treated her harshly, she would stop by the Kempock stane as she wandered home, and strike it with an old cloth, saying:

"I knock this rag upon this stane.

To raise the wind in the de'ils name.

It shall not lye till I please again."

And she would send this wind upon her masters home, causing the rafters to shake and the kye to run. Such were the tricks that Mary played in  her early days of witching.

And then, some two our more years after joining the coven, Mary attended a midnight  meeting at Katies house. As the wind and rain battered around the little cottage, the coven sat in front of the fire and talked about all that they had done the past week, discussing whom would be the next subject of their mischief.  And then some time later, their came a loud knock at the door. No-one was expected, and Katie was in fear of answering it. The room fell silent. Again the door was knocked, and still Katie was not for answering. And then upon the third knock, Katie stood up, as if in a trance, and walked slowly to the door, unlocking the latch.

As the door creaked open, who was standing there but the De'il himself, tail between his legs, and horns poking out from out under his tall top hat. Coated black in the soot from the fires of hell, he stood there with a bold grin on his face, and in his thick slow treacle voice, he asked:

"May I come in?"

And Katie nodded. Bold as brass he hopped into the cottage, bidding Katie to shake his hand, which she did. Mary took fright at the whole scene, and would have left there and then if she could have. But the De'il had her in his trance, and there was ought she could do. He gave them wine and bread, and soon they were all very merry indeed. And then he bid Mary to dance with him. Oh if only she had said no. But she didn't. She took him by the hand and the two danced a merry jig around the room. And the De'il spoke to her thus:

"Since you would not tell me your name all those years ago, I'll give you a new one. Y'ur Mary no more. Clowts shall be y'ur name. And you shall call

me Serpent."

Mary, under his spell now, was pleased with her new name, and as they danced round and round, she shouted it out loud enough for all of Innerkip to hear. Aye, for sure Mary received the mark of the De'il that night. And afterwards the people of the village would be heard to say:

"This lass is surely bewitched. Some mischief has befallen her, and I fear she is in the devil's grasp now."

Many hours would Clowts spend with her new master, roaming the parish, flying over the hills with him to do ill and harm to good God fearing folk. One evening, the coven met at the old gate house, down among the forest of Ardgowan. Here the De'il sent them to the shore for sand, which he bade them cast around the ministers house, so that they might better bewitch him. Then he shook his hands above their heads, and they were turned into cats, and roamed through the houses of the village. Such were the deeds that the coven performed in the service of the De'il. But in this business, some were followers, others chiefs. And Mary was one such chief.

Of all the witches of Innerkip, she was surely her masters favourite. What misfortune, to find yourself in favour with the De'il. But such was Mary's lot.

One dark and stormy night, the witches met under the shadow of the old Kempock stane. Here they lit a fire, and took turns to tell tales of old, of the lost Gods and of things long forgotten. Long did they whisper of the forgotten forest spirits, of Lorne and of the little folk. But favourite among the tales told, was that of the Lady Clutha, the Serpent of the Clyde who the ancients once worshipped at the stone. And Mary looked at the stone and said:

"Sure, is it not a fit stone for a Serpent?"

"Aye Clowts; it is," answered Katie.

"But would it not look even better in the river?" said Mary, with the look of the De'il in her eyes. So then and there, the young girl pledged that the coven should cast the stone into the Clyde in order that they might do damage to the fishermen and their boats. Oh have mercy on the lost soul, for with this promise, her fate was truly sealed. And they all laughed long and loud at this idea, and merrily they danced widdershins round the old stone, till the De'il himself arrived. They made merry long into the night, and when they went away, the De'il kissed each one of them. What poor souls, to be trapped under his spell.

However, word of the witchery had soon travelled well beyond the boundaries of the parish, and on the first day of March in the year 1662, the Privy Council, the most powerful body in all the land, sent Archibald Stewart, together with a great many others, to determine the root of the

Devilry that haunted Innerkip. They left no stone unturned in their search for the witches, and there wasn't a soul in the Parish who wasn't brought before them. Again and again the men of the Privy Council heard Mary's name mentioned, and so finally they ordered that she be brought before them. And there in the church house they kept her under locked key, asking for her confession of witchery. But she would give it not..

For days she stayed there, alone in a little room, with no-one to talk to, nor food to eat. And fever soon took its hold on her, and she began to see and hear strange things. And she would talk to herself too. Oh what a sorry state she was in. So pale and sickly. Then, on the evening of the third day, as Mary lay on her bed, she perceived the Ghost of her mother standing at the door, staring at her with a sad look on her face. In a voice as soft as wind, the ghost whispered:

"Oh Mary, did I not tell you not to stray from the path?"

The spectre vanished as quickly as it had appeared, and in a flash of white light, everything became clear to Mary and she lamented all her sins. Tired and hungry, the young girl offered up her confession to the Privy council. But it was too late. Mary was destined for the pyre, whether she confessed or not. Alone and sad, she could not help but feel cheated. A victim of misfortune and witchery at the hands of the De'il. And the thought of this brought tears to her eyes. Then, in a puff of smoke, the Serpent was at her ear again, sitting bold as brass on the bed next to her.

"Ah Clowts, thou has't but one hour to live, and then thy soul is mine for ever."

"No. I am Clowts nae more. I am Mary. Mary. And my soul is my ane."

The De'il stared into her eyes, his scaly red face just visible by the light of the candle.

"It matters not what thy name is. You are still damned."

Then he stood up and left the room, and none in the church house were ever the wiser about him being there. Imagine. The De'il under their own roof! He laughed loud and clear that night as he skipped merrily back to hell. Or so they say.

And then morning arrived, and the men of the council came for Mary. A great crowd had gathered in the square, around the large wooden stake. As she was marched towards it, the villagers taunted her, spitting on her and crying out "Burn the witch. Burn the witch." Then she was tied to the post, and the men of the privy council, looked on with justified hearts and minds. And Archibald Stewart addressed her thus:

"Mary Lamont, thou has been accused of thirteen counts of witchcraft, and of conspiring with the De'il, to which you have offered confession. For these crimes, thy punishment shall be burning at the stake. Do you wish to plead forgiveness for thy soul, witch?"

And with a tear in her eye, Mary looked up at  him and said:
"Tis all the same to be called a witch, as counted one. But I say, a witch I am not."
"Then your fate is sealed."
And with that, they advanced on the pyre, torches brandished with pious intent.  The rope was tightened round her neck, and the flames set. The smoke engulfed her, and in the misty haze, all clarity of vision was lost; Mary's mind became clouded with fear, and she seemed to lose herself. In the distance she could hear voices; "Burn the witch. Burn the witch." Then a warm light passed over her, and for a moment she was a little girl again, and her soul was lightened and set free. She never felt them break her neck, nor did she suffer as the heat of the flames purged the last drop of life from her body. For she was already far away, lost in a dream of a happier life, without sadness or fear. And may she rest there in peace.

For Mary

# Little Drummer Boy

*A drummer boy returns from a war he did not start;*
*three witches see to it that he will not return home safe from his duty...*

This is a time without a date, a year nobody was born, an era which would only be dimly recalled in a future age as "long, long ago."

Many things are not sure here. Many things are vague. What is true is this; the wind and mist flowing down toward this valley from the hills is very real indeed, brought from the highlands by forces not yet understood. The land under the feet of these three shadowed, robed figures can be counted upon, can be trusted. And, most importantly, the noise, moving closer now, steadily toward them, like a heart on two legs; a drum.

A nose is raised to the air, gulping in great gusts and sighing. "Boy. A boy. *Fresh.*" This last syllable drawn out obscenely, the voice full of unmended cracks and ancient dust; a crone.

"You can't be sure." A warm voice, but somehow unfriendly, rolling out and daring to be defied; a mother.

"She knows. She always knows." Young, this one, overconfident, and darkly pretty in this autumn cold; a maiden.

And still the drumbeat grows; swelling as a hungry heart might indeed do, carried on the cruel wind.

The boy's step should be light, his head held high; he feels this to be true, and yet he cannot make himself skip, cannot make a pleasant face. He already finds it difficult to remember the name of the war he returns home from, or the reason it was fought; what reasons do men need?

Still, this boy, this fine boy, he did his duty when called on by these men. It was impressed upon him; the importance, the *weight*, of his task in the weeks and months ahead. But the task itself is, too, already fading from his mind. The faces of his family, instead, hold foremost prominence for him. They flash again and again in his head, and it is this alone which almost gives him leave to smile, almost lightens his heart. But somehow not enough. Somehow not enough.

"I want him. I can take him." The crone's voice grows thick with a vile hunger, childlike in its affirmations. "I can!"

The maiden seems uninterested, concentrating on the fire the three women have made in this sacred place; she stabs out at the embers with a branch, causing a flurry of red-winged sparks to fly up, merging with the grey smoke, made purple by the night. "You'll never make the change. *You're* not strong enough."

The maiden's tone is just right for her purposes; mocking yet light. The crone takes the bait, white froth flying from her lips in anger; "I'll be showing you strong soon enough! Strong!"

"You don't even make sense." The maiden remains coquettish, playing with a lock of gold hair, lips twisted in a private joke. Her dainty head turns to the Mother briefly, though her eyes return to the fire which holds such fascination for her. "I think she might be losing her mind."

The mother does not give argument any more room to grow; she steps between the sisters, with a tone which might stop the growth of mountains. "Enough of this! We'll have the boy right enough. I'll take him."

"You?" The maiden stops her voice just short of total disbelief; she has some sense, it seems.

"Look in the flames you love so much and tell me if you see otherwise." The golden hair flickers and dances in the firelight as the young woman lowers her gaze, shifts her eyes left and right strangely. The red-orange firelights reflect in her sky-blue eyes, shifting and changing in them to form unreal shapes. Finally, she blinks, once, convulsively, and returns her eye line to her companions, and nods mutely.

"Then it's decided." There is an eerie calm in the mother's voice, somehow more terrible that the crone's hunger or the maiden's indifference.

The air around them seems suddenly sharper, crisper; the fire flares up, once, then seems about to die, and then all is normal once more.

The mother raises her arms to the sky and calls on a master she knows all too well, asks for his black blessing for the task ahead.

When the change comes, her two companions merely watch, not transfixed, not repulsed or fascinated; they watch. That is all.

The boy (he remembers his name, of course, who could forget such a thing) is still beating on his drum as it hangs at his hip; he does not know why. Perhaps he uses it to keep away things which would harm him; a skin-stretched talisman, beating away the dark. Perhaps he misses the war whose name he no longer knows. He is a young boy; he can be forgiven these forgettings.

Perhaps he is only a boy, beating on a drum. This, too, is a possibility.

The thought that he is only a player, a part of a larger game, his fate even in these next few moments sealed and decided in a time long before this; an unspeakable idea. Unspeakable.

The mother is gone, her robes and raiment torn and scattered by the fire. Where she stood is a coal-black wolf, ten feet from snout to stop. No wolf such as this ever stalked the highlands of this land, however; its eyes are filled with a fire no man could face, and in the dark rustlings of its thick

pelt is the very emptiness of space. Its lips pull back from freakish, dripping teeth, a growl fit for a titan beginning deep in a stomach which would surely accommodate any innocent foolish enough to cross its path; aye, happily enough.

As it stops, sniffs once at the night air, and lopes off down the earthen trail with an unspeakable hunger slobbering from its lips, the two women by the fire look at each other, once, over the dying fire.

The boy hears and smells the beast before he sees it; the wind brings him its horrible footpads and each and every noisome breath. Nevertheless, his breath catches in his throat at the sight of it, racing toward him, slowing, slowing, stopping. Stopping and staring, a black growling patch of night in the road ahead. Eyes that could strip a man's soul lock on his own blue eyes, and they know him utterly.

This boy, just a boy, a drummer boy, walking home, keeps walking; he lifts his foot, takes a step. Another. Another. Moving closer to this beast, this escapee from the worst of his midnight dreams. I know not why he does this; I merely tell you.

All the while, with every step, he beats his drum.

Beat.

Beat.

Beat.

The animal lunges, a growl as vast as the sky raising in its throat.

The rest is nightmare.

# The Orchard

A short playlet demonstrating the consequences of lying
and the folly of learned men...

"Magic terrors, spells of mighty power
Witches who rove at the midnight hour."

Characters
Spirit -              a narrator
James Brisbane -  a witchhunter
Christian Shaw -   a young girl
John Lindsay -      a farmer
The Minister -      a doctor and friend to the Shaw family
Accused -           six poor souls
Demon -             a little devil

Enter SPIRIT.

SPIRIT
(to audience)
I am a Spirit and am charged to tell you the sorry tale of Christian Shaw
and those her actions took from us. In the year of our lord sixteen hundred
and ninety seven, the witchfinder James Brisbane travelled to Erskine
parish, trailing murder in his wake.

Enter BRISBANE.

BRISBANE
I am here as representative of a commision to His Majesty's Privy Council.
This commission has been informed of several flagrant grounds of suspicion
of witches and witchcraft in the shire of Renfrew, most especially from the
afflicted and extraordinary condition of one Christian Shaw, daughter of
John Shaw of Bargarran.

SPIRIT
The girl, Christian Shaw has named a local farmer John Lindsay as the
force behind the evils which are tormenting her.

Enter LINDSAY with ACCUSED who stand stage left.

SPIRIT
And here is John Lindsay now. A good man, held by the commission

without warrant. Those with him are accused as members of his coven.
All are damned, and we can but bear witness to the misdeeds of those we
charge to protect us.

SPIRIT exits.

BRISBANE
You are John Lindsay?

LINDSAY
I am.

BRISBANE
And you are aware of the evils you are said to have engaged in?

LINDSAY
I am aware that there are those evil minded enough to think me capable
of such things.

BRISBANE
It is said, and many here know it to be true, that you and your coven do
meet in the orchard of John Shaw of Bargarran at twilight, there to consort
with a black grim man. What say you John Lindsay?

LINDSAY
I am often in the fields at twilight if my days work there is not done. But
God as my witness I am there alone

BRISBANE
You dare call on our Lord to defend you.

LINDSAY
If not he, then who?

BRISBANE
Perhaps the dark man you worship in the orchard! Does he not protect his
own?
Let us remind John Lindsay of the torments endured by Christian Shaw.

Enter MINISTER who stands stage right.

BRISBANE
Minister, I would ask you to describe the ungodly afflictions suffered by
the girl Christian Shaw. Those which she suffers even now.

MINISTER
The girl is under a very sore and unnaturalike distemper, frequently seized
with strange fits, sometimes blind, sometimes deaf and dumb.

BRISBANE
She is possessed insensible.

MINISTER
The several parts of her body sometimes violently extended, and at other
times, as violently contracted.

MINISTER stops and is silent.

BRISBANE
What is wrong Minister?

MINISTER
Forgive me sir. For it is in the telling of these next events which I am
tested. Oh! For such fates to befall a girl so young and sweet as she.

BRISBANE
Go on man. God is with you.

MINISTER
Sir, these several weeks past the girl hath disgorged a considerable quantity
of...unnatural items.

BRISBANE
She has brought them forth in a sickness?

MINISTER
She has sir.

BRISBANE
And what manner of items would these be Minister?

MINISTER
There has been a considerable quantity of hair, folded up straw, unclean

hay, wild fowl feathers, the bones of some kind of fowl and all this together with a number of coal cinders, burning hot, candle grease and gravel stones.

BRISBANE points at LINDSAY

BRISBANE
What horrors! What horrors to visit upon one so young.

MINISTER
Also her skin is reddened and sore from a nipping.

BRISBANE
Bring her in! Bring in poor Christian Shaw. Who has, these past twenty hours, been prayed over constantly by the presbytery to exorcise the spirit brought down upon her by the coven of John Lindsay.

Enter SPIRIT

SPIRIT
And here she comes now. Does she know her lies will bear such bitter fruit? What is it that consumes her so, that prevents her from calling a halt to the tangled route of her ill intentions? But perhaps! Perhaps now she will, perhaps she will throw light on her lies and back upon the poor souls condemned.

Enter CHRISTIAN, hunched over and wrapped in a blanket. She stands stage right. BRISBANE walks to her, placing a hand upon her shoulder. She looks at him and nods.

SPIRIT
The seeds of a dark madness have been sown.

SPIRIT exits.

BRISBANE
You know me Christian. We are all here today in the sight of our lord to help you. You are often tormented are you not?

CHRISTIAN
For my sins sir.

BRISBANE
No child! These sins are not yours! You are tortured by those in service of
Satan. Do you know who it is who has brought this upon you?

CHRISTIAN
I do sir.

BRISBANE
Then speak it's name. Tell us all.

CHRISTIAN
Sir I cannot.

BRISBANE
Who lass? Who is it that torments you?

CHRISTIAN shakes her head

CHRISTIAN
I cannot.

BRISBANE
But you must. You must child. Else we shall never be rid of this demon.

CHRISTIAN begins crying.

BRISBANE
Would I could take your pain as mine child. But you must say it. You must
say the name of the one who torments you.

CHRISTIAN (screaming)
Sir it is John Lindsay who works upon me. He and those who stand with
him.

BRISBANE
John Lindsay! Is it John Lindsay who offends you girl?

CHRISTIAN is shuddering and howling

CHRISTIAN
It is! It is!

BRISBANE
See my Lords, how even the name of the creature wrenches at her eternal
soul!

Enter SPIRIT

SPIRIT
Had she soul left to lose? Or had her lying already brought her low? How,
how even now can she not to turn in the eyes of God and tell all of those
gathered that it is she that has been wrong. Would she be forgiven if she
did? Who can know, for time is now as short for Christian as it is for John
Lindsay. The Lord forgives all, but does a soul as dark  and twisted as
Christian's even seek forgiveness? A soul so filled with thorns?

SPIRIT exits.

BRISBANE
We have already heard of the ungodly terrors sent to torture poor Christian,
and we scarce need more proof than that. But the workings of Satan are
well documented, and it is known that he will place a mark on those in his
service.

MINISTER lifts the sleeve of LINDSAYS shirt.

BRISBANE
See here! The devils own mark. Minister, have you a pin. A long pin sir!
And sharp!

MINISTER
I do.

BRISBANE
Then bring it forth in full sight of the court.

MINISTER hands BRISBANE a pin.
BRISBANE attempts to stick the pin in the arm of LINDSAY. It breaks. He
addresses court.

BRISBANE
See! See how the devils mark cannot be punctured. Pins cannot prick it!
But I shall try again, that you might all see full well.

Again BRISBANE takes a pin. This one sticks in.

BRISBANE
Ah! Worse still. This time we pierce the foul mark, only to find we cannot draw blood!
There is no blood from this pin prick! Let us see if we can yet tease blood from this cursed scab.

SPIRIT enters.

SPIRIT
For hours, poor John Lindsay endured the pricking of pins. Fire was held to his arm to see if the devils mark would burn, and knives drawn across his skin to see if it could be cut.
And all the others suffered the same. How misguided the actions of self righteous men.

Behind SPIRIT, LINDSAY and ACCUSED are bound.

And at the end of the day, battered, burned and bloody, the session sentenced them to be burned at the Gallow Green in Paisley. Seven souls in total, one of whom took his own life rather than face the flames at the stake.

LINDSAY and ACCUSED scream and then exit.

But the souls of those destroyed by wicked men, found peace in heaven, while those who dealt in lies and torture were themselves condemned to that in turn.

DEMON enters and drags MINISTER, BRISBANE and CHRISTIAN off stage.

For I am the damned soul of the liar Christian Shaw, charged to forever wander by the Orchard where poor John Lindsay spent his days. And in telling you my sorry tale, I ask only for your forgiveness and that you would hesitate to persecute, where I did not.
Farewell.

SPIRIT exits.

CURTAIN

# WitchCraft

*Brewing the diabolical hell-broth*

Between the 10th and the 16th centuries, literally thousands of people were persecuted throughout Europe for alleged crimes of witchcraft. In Britain, witch-hysteria arrived at a relatively late date and the type of heretic-witch who was constantly pursued by the Inquisition in Europe was virtually unknown in Scotland, until a law was passed against them by Mary Queen of Scots in 1563. While in England the practise of burning witches was never really adopted, witches were burned in Scotland. Torture was used to gain confessions of guilt from them, another practice not widespread south of the border. The Protestant John Knox lived to see the Catholic Queen Mary lose her power, but the punishment of witches remained the same under the reformed church, and the persecution of witches was carried out with great enthusiasm. Upon his succession, James the sixth, Mary's son, developed a fixation about witchcraft. After his marriage in 1589, his life was threatened by a group of witches and they were burned to death as both traitors and heretics. Following this, he changed the wording of the act to include the following:

" If any person or persons shall use, practise or exercise any Invocation or Conjuration of any evil or wicked spirit, or shall consult, covenant with, entertain, employ, feed or reward any evil or wicked spirit to or for any intent or purpose; or take any dead man or child out of his or her grave, or the skin, bone or any other part of any dead person, to be employed or used in any manners of Witchcrafts ..... (they) Shall suffer the pains of death".

Although witch-hunting in Scotland continued sporadically between about 1500 and 1700, there were three main peak-periods of activity, 1590-97, 1640-44 and 1660-63, during which time accusation and paranoia were rife among the people.

## Early Trials

In Renfrewshire, there were witches before there were prosecutions, and of all the parishes, Inverkip, or Innerkip as it was then known, was the most infamous. The memory of the notorious Dunrod some thirty years previous was still present as the first of a new wave of cases came to light.
In mid-September, 1649, 'everie brother was ordained to cause search for one James Thomson, a vaiging beggar alleged to be ane Warlock.' Some two

weeks later the reverend of Inverkip, John Hamilton, reported his fears concerning witchcraft among his parishioners. Jean Scott, Janet Paterson and Janet Loudon of Inverkip were all ordered to be apprehended, as was Janet Galbraith of Greenock. At this time, 'it was appointed that severall brethren deall with the persons in prison for witchcraft at Paisley and Renfrew to bring them to confession.' The procedure for dealing with those alleged to be consorting with dark forces at this time appeared to consist of a lengthy stay in the cells, during which they were subjected to a variety of tortures in order to obtain a confession.

The hysteria surrounding witchcraft and devil-worship continued unabated for some time, and by the summer of 1650 a great deal many more alleged witches and warlocks had been apprehended throughout the county. On the 26th of July 1650, the Presbytery found 'Janey Hewison in Kilallan guiltye of divers points of sorcerie and witchcraft and seriouslie recommend her to the lords of Secret Council or committee of assembly that ane commission be granted for her tryall and punishment.'

However, most alleged witches were simply admonished and released, and soon the furor appeared to subside as quickly as it had surfaced.

## Mary Lamont

While there was a notable absence of trials over the next 12 years or so, the air of the supernatural must surely have been present in the minds of local people, even though they were no longer seeing witches on every street corner. Mary Lamont was a 5 year old girl when the events of 1649 disrupted life in her village, but at the age of 18, she would find herself at the centre of the area's most infamous witchcraft trial.

*The Daff Glen*

In 1662, Mary was accused of 13 counts of witchcraft, including dealings with the Devil. Of these charges, the most serious related to her involvement in a conspiracy to push the Kempock Stone into the river Clyde. At the time, the stone, often referred to as 'Granny Kempock,' was the focus of much local superstition. Sailors would leave offerings at the stone to ensure a safe passage, and marriages were not deemed lucky unless the couple had danced round the stone.

Mary's coven (consisting of herself and parishioners from Inverkip, Gourock and Greenock) believed that, by toppling the stone, they would disrupt shipping and fishing. It is also possible that their efforts were in some way connected to the serpent of the Clyde, to which the Kempock Stone is believed to be an altar.

Mary was brought before a tribunal

sanctioned by the Privy Council, and on the 4th of March 1662, she offered up her confession:

"She (Marie Lamont) came and offered herself willingly to the trial saying that God moved her heart to confess, because she had lived long in the devils service.

She confessed most ingeniously that five years since, Katherin Scott, in Murdiestean, within the parish of Innerkip, learned

*The Daff Glen*

her to take kyes milk, bidding her go out in misty mornings and take with her a harrie tedder, and draw it over the mouth of mug saying "In Gods name, God send us milk, God send it and meikle of it". By this means she and the said Katherin got much of their neighbours milk and made butter and cheise thereof.

She confessed two years and a half since, the devil came to the said Katherin Scott's house, in the midst of the night, where were present with them, Margaret McKenzie of Greenock, Janet Scot of Gourock, herself, and several others. The devil was in the likeness of a muckle black man, and sung to them, and they danced: he gave them wine to drink and wheat bread to eat and they were all very merrie. She confesses at that meeting, the said Ketie Scott made her first acquaintance with the devil, who caused her to drink with him, and shake hands with him.

She confesses that at that time, the devil bade her betake herself to his service, and it should be well with her, and bade her baptism, which she did, delivering herself wholly to him, by putting her one hand on the crown of her head, and the other hand to the sole of her foot, and giving all betwixt these two to him.

*Witches and their familiars, in the service of the Devil*

She confessed that at that time he gave her a new name, and called her Clowts, and bade her call him Serpent when he desired to speak with him.

She confessed that at the same time, the Devil nipped her on the right side, which was very painful for a time, but thereafter he stroked with his hand, and healed it, this she confesses to be his mark.

She confessed that when she had been at a meeting since Yule last, with the other witches, in the night, the devil convoyed her home in the dawning; and when she was come near the house wherein she was a servant, her master saw a waff of him as he went away from her.

She confessed that about five weeks since, Jean King, Kettie Scott, Janet Holm, herself and several others, met together in the night at the back gate of Ardgowan where the devil was with them in the likeness of a black man with cloven feet, and directed them to fetch white sand from the shore and cast it about the gates of Ardgowan, and about the Ministers house, but she says that when they were about this business, the devil turned them into the likeness of cats, by shaking his hands above their heads. She confesses, also that in business, some were chiefs and ringleaders, others were but followers.

She confessed also that she was with Kettie Scott, Margaret McKenzie and others at a meeting at Kempock, where they intended to cast the long stone into the sea thereby to destroy boats and ships; where also they danced, and the Devil kissed them when they went away."

At the time, the irreverent nature of the acts the young woman claimed to have carried out greatly shocked the local populace, and the case quickly became notorious throughout the country.

*The Kempock Stone*

In the minds of her accusers, a case as grave as this demanded swift and vengeful justice. Mary Lamont was strangled, and her body was burned at the stake, thus bringing to a close one of the most regrettable chapters in the history of the parish.

### The Possession of Christian Shaw

The third epidemic of witchcraft in the area again first broke out in Inverkip, and on the third of July 1695, it was brought before the presbytery by Sir Archibald Stewart of Ardgowan. He accused John Dougall of "maist scandalous carriage in using charmes and such like things." It was claimed of Dougall "that he taught one how to make his own corn to grow, and his neighbours' to go back" and "he made his own corn to grow and sowed sour milk amongst it on baltaneday". He was to be convened before the congregation of Inverkip, publicly rebuked and declared to be a scandalous person. Involved in this trial was the minister of Kilmacolm, one James Brisbane. Brisbane was

*A witch-hunter*

appointed to Kilmacolm in November of 1693 and he had long been concerned with witchcraft. Strangely enough, the accusations throughout the county happened only while Brisbane was in residence and after he moved away from Kilmacolm, the cases faded as quickly as they had began.

The most famous of the incidents in which Brisbane was involved was the possession of Christian Shaw. In the year of 1696 Christian, young daughter of John Shaw, the Laird of Bargarran in Erskine, was victim to what is surely the most well-remembered cases of 'demonic possession' in Scottish history. It resulted in a large number of local people being implicated as her tormentors. As terrible as the grisly resolution of this case was, it seemed to bring to an end the hysteria in Renfrewshire concerning witches and witchcraft.

The terrible symptoms of the eleven-year-old Christian's illness certainly seemed to indicate to all around her that she was the victim of some dark force. Her minister at the time told how she was "under a very sore and unnaturallike distemper, frequently seized with strange fits, sometimes blind, sometimes deaf and dumb. The several parts of her body sometimes violently extended, and at other Times as violently contracted." Her skin was also marked and nipped, and she would take violent fits, during which she would mention the name of those tormenting her.

In January 1697, when Christian's health did not improve, it was decided by the Lords of HM Privy Council to set up a commission to investigate "being informed of several flagrant grounds of suspicion of witches and witchcraft in the shire of Renfrew, especially from the afflicted and extraordinary condition of Christian Shaw, daughter of John Shaw of Bargarran."

The commission included Alexander Blantyre and Alexander Porterfield of Duchal, as well as Robert Semple, sheriff depute of Renfrew and Sir John Shaw of Greenock, cousin of Bargarran, and uncle to Christian Shaw.

In Kilmacolm there was a moor which was said to be a popular haunt for witches. There they would have dealings with the devil, and cast spells upon the local parishioners. The previous year, Janet Woodrow was apprehended on suspicion of being a witch. However civil powers were lax in prosecuting, and Janet returned to Kilmacolm to continue her 'hellish pranks.' It was to this area that Brisbane returned a year later when hunting for the tormentors of Christian Shaw. First among those named was John Lindsay, a local farmer, who was subsequently held without warrant by the Commission after being accused as the head of a coven. A further five members of the 'coven' were arrested. It was believed at the time that the witches met at Shaw's Orchard at twilight. Here they were said to have summoned 'the black dugs o' the Deil,' which then roamed free over the countryside to summon other witches and warlocks to the midnight meetings. Furthermore, Elizabeth Anderson of Kilmacolm, the youngest accused of the coven, is said to have conspired with her father and grandmother to bewitch Mr. William Fleming, minister of Inverkip.

The commission was swift to bring these seven individuals to trial, despite the fact that, retrospectively, there seems to have been an ulterior motive to Christian's accusations. During the trial, many strange tests were inflicted on the suspects, which yielded equally strange results. The members of the alleged coven were repeatedly pricked with pins which would either bend, doing no damage, or pierce the skin drawing no blood. This was seen as ample evidence that the seven had 'The Devil's Mark" on their body.

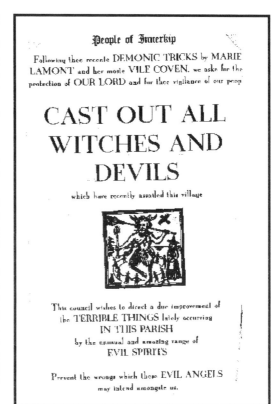

*A typical call for a witch-hunt.*

As a result of the young girls testimony and the trial, 3 men and 4 women were sentenced to be burned to death at the Gallow Green in Paisley. A short time later, it became apparent that everyone had overreacted to what became regarded as nothing more than the disturbed fantasies of a young girl. The cases went some way to ending the hysteria and by 1736, all the Scottish Witchcraft Acts were repealed, bringing to a close this dark episode in our nations history.

*The Witches hanged*

# MARKET CROSS

*An unfortunate thief meets a rebel hero at the Greenock Market...*

Jim Dewar was a thief. He always had been a thief, and perhaps he always would be a thief, but one thing was certain; for all the time he had spent *being* a thief, he certainly hadn't developed a talent for thieving. Which was a shame, as this was generally considered essential for his chosen occupation. He did not come from a long family tradition of thieves, Jim was self taught, and this was perhaps where his problem lay, for as anyone who knew him would tell you, Jim Dewar was daft as an empty bucket. The ship was sailing, but the anchor was still down if you see what I mean. His complete lack of skill had ensured more than a few stints in the docks, in fact, if he wasn't there on a Monday morning waiting to get pelted, folk would be enquiring after his wellbeing.

There was plenty who would plead with him to mend his ways, or at the very least, to get better at stealing things, for everyone could see he was bound for the gallows sooner or later.
"Aye" he would say "Still ye might as well get hung fur a sheep as fur a spud."
Thing is, he would most likely get hung for a spud. There was no way Jim would ever have been able to organise stealing a sheep. The sheep would have had to be in on the plan.

Now, nobody knows what it was he'd stolen that day, I've heard a few folk say it was some sort of magic charm that used to belong to a local landowner, others say it was a tiny wee acorn, made out of gold. Most say it was in fact, a sack full of pig guts. He was probably going to try to put them back together to make a whole pig.

It was Market Day, and so all the stalls were down by the cross at the shore. It was a beautiful day, there were plenty of ships in, and everyone's wandering around just enjoying the sunshine and smiling. I was having a word with this big tall fellow, he was looking to buy a jerkhin of some sort, but he was right broad, almost square. And his arms were that long, that he looked out of proportion. I would never have said this to the gentleman in question of course, as he looked like the sort that could handle himself. So I was trying my best to find something suitable for a man as ungainly as he, and this is when Jim comes thundering into view, knocking over as many kids and old folk as aren't quick enough to get out of his road. As

soon as I saw him, I kept my head down, but he had spotted me right away and he comes flying over to my stall.

"They're after me." he says "I'm fur the drop this time. You've got tae help. Get me on a ship. Or even on a horse."

I was a little annoyed, and I suggested to Jim rather sharply, that he calm down.

"I've been summoned but." says Jim "They've summoned me tae the market cross."

At this, the big tall fellow chips in.

"Then I suggest my friend, that you don't try and find passage by boat."

"How no?" asks Jim, a little perturbed by this turn of events.

The big chap goes on to explain, that the whole point of summoning someone to the market cross is because it's the only place you can arrest someone of no fixed abode. And Jim's been living outdoors for a goodly number of months, following an unfortunate incident when he was caught stealing his landlady's scones. They were still cooking at the time, you could hear him screaming all down Cartsdyke.

Our man then informs us that it is common practice for the militia to offer ships Captains a reward for apprehending anyone trying to leave town to avoid the summons to the cross.

This takes Jim a few moments to digest, and by the time he's finally understood it enough to start panicking about what he's going to do, I can already see the militia at the other end of the market.

Thing is, when I turned back to warn him, both Jim and the big lad are off. And so's the jerkhin.

Jim, I've never seen since, there's a few people have told me he was hanged for stealing a butter churn. He probably meant to steal a cow.

I've seen the big fellows face a few times since though, on wanted posters. Rob Roy.

And to think, he stole a jerkhin from my wee stall. I just hope it fitted him okay.

# MARKET CROSS

## THE GROWTH OF A TOWN

In 1635, a charter was granted by Charles I to Sir John Shaw of Greenock, which erected Greenock into a burgh of barony. By this charter, full powers were conferred upon Shaw to choose bailiffs, clerks, sergeants and other officers. This was the first step towards Greenock establishing itself as a township.

Greenock's prosperity was boosted by the Union of 1707; before this Union the small town had a population of around 1000, and a small harbour which could only receive fishing boats. Lady Shaw, who was conversant with the affairs of the town, would later say:

"In the year 1700, there was no harbour there but a heap of whin stones for shading the fishers' boats and small barques; the bay was the only protection that small vessels had to anchor in this close to town."

The people of Greenock had, in 1700, petitioned Parliament for financial assistance in construction of a new harbour, but were refused. Seeing the Union as a new opportunity, however, the townsfolk spent £5,600 on improved harbour facilities. This saw trade and fishing income begin to grow; indeed, the main industry of the town of Greenock continued to be herring fishing, a fact marked by the town's unusual coat of arms at the time; a design of two crossed herrings, along with the legend 'May herring swim which trade maintains.' in 1714 a custom house was established, and marked profits began to be shown by 1740 once the construction debts had been repaid. Soon after this, the town made an application to Parliament to obtain the power to extend the scale of the harbour, and this time were successful; in 1751, an Act was passed stating that two Scots pence from every pint brewed or sold in the town would go to repair and extension of the harbour, along with construction of a church, market, town house and such. This would be the starting point for Greenock's growth as a port of trade and industry.

## THE MARKET CROSS

One privilege granted to towns granted the status of a Burgh of barony was the licence to erect a town cross; the original intention of this, passed down from the church and the monarchy, was to 'inspire men with a sense of morality and piety in their daily avocations of life.' Subsequent to its construction, all transactions, sales or trades of value to be carried out in the town were begun, and often ended at, the Market Cross. This stood at the corner of Cross-shore and Shaw street and was marked by four stones bearing the date 1669, marked out with white pebbles. Here goods were bought and sold on a weekly basis, and prior to the reformation no business could be conducted until the town officials had settled on a price for each item being sold. As the town grew, so too did the market, and with so many ships arriving it soon became a thriving centre of commerce. Yet like all sea ports, Greenock was attracting it's fair share of thieves, vagabonds and colourful characters, including among others, Rob Roy, who is said to have raided the market for cattle. At this time there existed a curious law which stated that a person could only be arrested in their own home or somewhere they had lived for over forty days. However, if the accused was not a Scottish citizen, or had no fixed abode, then the only place they could be apprehended was the market cross. Here, summons for the accussed were posted so that ships captains would know not to take them as passengers.

*The Anchor Inn near the site of the original Market Cross*

# THE MERMAID

"Mugwort. Mugwort's best for consumption. Anyone'll tell you that. And you'd do well to take heed of that advice, as there's so many pretty young things droppin' dead these days.

No of course it doesn't taste nice, nothin' that's good for you ever does. But if it's a choice between that or being down in the ground I know which I'd rather.

Do you know Robert Chambers? Right. Well, ask him and he'll tell you himself, but a few weeks past there, he happened to be at the funeral of a young one like yourself. Ellen something? I can't remember. Anyhow, it was consumption that got her. And the procession happened to be passing along the Port Glasgow high road on the shore side. So as you can imagine it's all very sombre and sad, her being such a young thing, and the Priest's leadin' them in prayer as they walk, when all of a sudden, someone starts singing. And it's very high pitched, and it's not really the time for it, so everyone's lookin' around to see who it is. And it's Robert who notices, and he points out to the river. And there's a mermaiden, head peepin' out of the water, she's the one singing. The priest and all the bearers turn to see her, and when she's sure she's got everyone's attention, she says

'If they had drank nettles in March

An' eat muggins in May

Sae many braw maidens

Wadna gang tae the clay'

Muggins. Mugwort. There even mermaids will tell you.

So you hold on to these, and I'll boil up some nettles."

Kidd's Tale

*A good Greenock man, turned to bad deeds for the sake of men who*
*will never swing for them, sits in a gaol and tells a man his tale.*
*Who tells another man. Who tells another man...*

## The Barman

Haven't seen a night like this in all my life, and Old John's seen a few
nights, I can tell you. Ask anyone; they'll tell you. Been here longer than
most of these old sots can remember, wash my mouth out with soap and
water.

Never been emptier than tonight; I can usually rely on Tom and Puckle in
the corner putting paid to the problems of the world over a pint of ale, but
this storm has even made those two share their drinks and stories at
home over a fire. Pity; I like a bit of company in the evenings, but never
mind. The weather will clear tomorrow, I'm sure, and then all of the empty
chairs tonight will be filled with people who'll remember how much they
like a drink.
Still, never bother; five more minutes and then even I might just get tired
of waiting and head off to my warm bed.

Oh-ho; what's this though? I might think it was a drowned cat out of the
rain for a bowl of warm milk and a heat if it weren't standing on its own
two legs. The man staggers in, a quick timely flash of lightning outside
illuminating his haggard face for a brief second, and I take a step backward,
this old barkeep who's seen a few sights (ask anyone; they'll tell you)
shocked in his shoes by a rain-soaked traveller.

The man turns toward me slowly, and he must see by my face that I think
him a ghost or demon sent by the storm to take my life (or, worse, my
pub) because he smiles, his face suddenly like a skull. He slams down on
the bar a knapsack that looks as if it's been on his back three times round
the world, and he sits down heavily.
"What have you in those bottles for a man who's just seen his cousin
hanged twice?"
Well, I don't shock easy, but this makes me pause just a moment, before
I draw down a bottle of whisky that hasn't been drained in a goodly while
(the dust on the cork must be twelve year old), and I set it down with two
glasses. It surely doesn't look like this poor creature can afford such fine
malt, but he surely looks like he needs it, and now that I've seen his
hunted face, I surely do too. I pour the amber liquid into the glasses and
I say the thing I must have said every night for most of my long life to

some weary soul or another.
"Why don't you tell Old John about it."

### The TRAVELLER

My story is like most others; it ends in horror and heartache, and leaves the listener with more questions than answers. But I will tell you anyway. Perhaps if I tell someone this gnawing feeling at my very gut will move on and leave me in peace.

I have just this day returned from London, where I had travelled off my own back to visit my cousin on the night before his slaughter. Now you might not think this any particular thing, for in these days many men hang for their crimes, but if I tell you that this crime was piracy and treason, and this man William Kidd, then perhaps you begin to take shape of my story in your head, barkeep.
Another drink? Yes. I think so. I think so.

William was blind drunk already by the time they let me see him on a warm evening at the gaol. His only requests to his captors were for more drink, and he shouted cursewords at all and sundry, even for a short while mistaking me for an English guard.
When by and by William had calmed down he began to tell me his tale, a story filled with bitterness and recriminations, the story of a man betrayed and humiliated, of turncoats and bloodshed. It was a tale that in other circumstances I might have paid a penny to sit and listen to in an alehouse, if it did not concern my own flesh and blood.

### The Pirate

Are you really there, cousin? I cannot see you. I drink and drink to close my eyes so they will not see the eyes of the man who nooses my neck on the morrow. I hope it works.
I am sorry that I have not been home for many a year now; New York has been my home out of necessity, and I ofttimes yearn for Greenock's waters and her folks. But now it is too late. Never to look into my family's eyes again. Never.

You there! Bring me some more of this! And some for my guest! Quick about it now. Has your master not told you to obey the whims of the dying man?

It saddens me to think that these sheeplike oafs will be the last people I clap eyes on afore I go on. Yes, cousin. You are here too. I thank you. You

are most kind.

We have not much time now. I have to pass on the tale of my betrayal to
a friendly soul. I will tell you some things, and then I will give you something,
and then you must go, cousin. Do not stay to watch me dance the hempen
jig. I beseech you. But stay now, if you are not of hard heart, and listen to
the things I must impart.

I never set out in life to be the blackguard and thief they paint me to be.
I was appointed by Richard Coote, Earl of Bellamont, to protect the British
Isles from pirates, but curse me, I was taken in by the romance of the high
seas, cousin. I decided once I had seen the wealth available from looting
these ships off the East coast of the dark continent that this was to be the
life for me. God would forgive me. He has surely forgiven worse.

But that is not the darkest part of my tale, cousin. Surely not. The King
himself gave me leave to raid French ships as they were enemies of Britain,
and even a licence to this regard. A licence, if you cen believe that! But
nonetheless. I am never a man to look a gift cow in the mouth, and so
with this happy arrangement set up, and with several benefactors, chief
among them Lord Bellamont, supporting me in my endeavours in exchange
for a small share of the loot, things were right sweet for a good while.

For a while, that is, until the Adventure Galley. God, but I never hope to
sail in such a tub again! Such a rotten pile of timbers I've never captained,
and the crew were worse. Picked up in New York  by a lazy first mate (for
a pint of ale each, I reckon), they began to plot against me from the start.
I even had to kill one o' them to teach them a lesson. Never meant to kill
him, but the man, Gunner Moore they called him, came at me with a
chisel. Picked up a bucket and brained him right there. Never meant to
kill him. And they call me a murderer for that.
Cousin, here I am getting off the point again. Suffice to say things rocked
along roughly for a little while; lootings were thin on the ground and poor
food stores had the men sick as dogs and angry as bears. When eventually
we raided two goodly rich French ships, the crew were so near the end of
their tether they took more than their share of the treasure and deboarded
in New York never to be seen again.
Well! Here was I in a good pickle. I had to tell Lord Bellamont that I had no
doubloons for him; I span him my hard luck story, and he was not right
happy, but that was that. And the next thing I know, there's a bloody
warrant out for my arrest! 'Piracy and Murder', they say! Why if the King
himself doesn't know I'm a pirate! If he doesn't himself condone a little

murdering in the name of patriotism! It fair makes you sick.

All sorts of lies they spread about me. Lord Bellamont himself said that I took all the loot for myself (which was NOT from French ships, but stolen from the slit pockets of innocent murdered men, so he says), and murdered my crew! Cousin! I see from your wide eyes you feel the same as me on this matter, do you not? Do you not?

I was fair doomed from there. The judge would not let me appoint a lawyer to defend me, and so I took it to task myself. I found two good crewmen who would speak of my fair name, but they changed their stories and stabbed me in the back (spurred on by the dirty money of Bellamont, I dare say, cousin). Each lie blackening my reputation as a gentleman pirate brought me a step closer to the gallows, with nothing I could do to slow my pace.

And here we are, cousin. Tomorrow I die. Three words which strike fear in my very soul, unable to bear were it not for the good gallon of ale in my belly. It is late now, cousin, and they say you must go soon. But I told you I was going to give you a gift, and I shall.

Lord Bellamont is fair clever, but never more so than a good Greenock man can be, eh, cousin? For before I returned to Boston to my expected arrest, I buried the remaining Adventure Galley treasure. I offered it to Bellamont in exchange for my freedom, but the scoundrel would not accept. So now I give this to you to return to my wife, cousin. Let her die a rich fat lady instead of a hungry waif. Let me do this one thing before I meet my unrighteous end. Say you will.

Say you will.

## The TRAVELLER

And so I watched my cousin, William Kidd, a good man of Greenock born, hanged by the neck, against his very wishes. I simply could not leave without seeing it. I cannot explain why.

They had to hang him twice, did you know that? The rope snapped - an act of God, for Christ's sake - but they simply strung him up again, a man unable even to stand, and killed him for their rich masters. It sickens me.

What's that you say? The gift? Aah, there's the thing, Old John. I cannot tell you, good sir, as much as I appreciate your kindly ear and sweet whisky. That must go to William's wife this very night, or my life be as worthless as his. Speaking of which, I must away, for I hear the wind die down, and miles are before me on this night. Good night to you.

### The Barman

There he goes, my weary traveller, and not one word of his tale did I believe, I'll tell you that for a tanner. I've heard true and I've heard false, has Old John. Ask anyone; they'll tell you.

Oh-ho though; what's this? Must have fallen out of the fellow's bag as he left. Crumpled and torn and been in the water; but a map's a map for a'that, so they might say. And is that the word .... Hispaniola? No; impossible. A joke is what this is. And still...the traveller might still be outside; the wind is not low enough for him to have gotten far. I might give it back to him.

I might.

# Captain Kidd

"You may have heard of one Captain Kidd......the many stories current - the thousand vague rumors afloat about money buried, somewhere upon the Atlantic coast, by Kidd and his associates."

Edgar Allen Poe, *The Gold Bug.*

William James Kidd was reputedly born in a house on the corner of West Blackhall Street and Westburn Street, in 1645, later, rather fittingly, this would become the site of a newsagent named 'The Smuggler's Chest.'

Kidd was the son of a strict Presbyterian minister, and it has often been suggested that Kidd's piracy was an act of rebellion against his overbearing father. Certainly, the fact that he lived in a busy seaport town would have made a life on the open sea a more tempting proposition. No exact date is known for the beginning of Kidd's seafaring career, although by 1690 he had become established as a shipowner

*A galleon similar to the type used by Kidd*

in colonial New York, presumably having spent the intervening years on the high seas.

In 1695 Kidd, known only as a well-to-do New York colonist returned to Britain hoping to serve his King as captain of a Royal Navy warship. While Kidd waited in England for a vessel to command, the Whig-dominated Board of Trade pondered a related concern—the pirates who were disrupting commerce between England and her Indian colonies. The King's advisors decided that what was needed was an aggressive privateer who could battle the pirates on their own terms, and perhaps prey on a few French merchantmen as the opportunity arose. Fatefully enough the Board reached this conclusion almost as Kidd came knocking on the door, asking for a ship to command

Kidd was initially unwillingly to accept, wishing to hold out for a more legitimate commission in the Royal Navy. However his reluctance was interpreted as a sign of disloyalty towards the King and it was hinted that should he refuse, he would have no hope of ever obtaining a post in the Kings Navy. Thus Kidd was persuaded to accept the position of an officiated privateer.

At this time one of his strongest backers was Richard Coote, Earl of Bellamont, later to become Governor of Massachusetts Bay. This commission, issued by King William himself, granted Kidd the power to apprehend "pirates, free-

*Kidd and his cronies bury their loot*

booters, and sea-rovers, being our subjects or of other nations associated with them." The booty taken from these pirates would be returned to Boston, where it would be divided among the principals in this venture. This idea would be backed by the king, reasoned the plotting rogues, because an alarming rise in piracy was putting a crimp in England's supply line. If the King could see a way of reducing piracy while contributing to his own dwindling money supply, he would surely take it.

If Kidd encountered any resistance from the pirates, he was encouraged "by force to compel them to yield." He was also given a special "commission of reprisals" that justified his taking French ships, an authorization given to him because England was involved in a war with France.

There was one condition to the agreement; Kidd was ordered never to attack the ships of any country allied with the English. "We do strictly charge and command you, as you will answer the contrary at your peril, that you do not, in any manner, offend or molest our friends or allies, their ships or subjects, by colour or pretence of these presents, or the authority granted."

*A Map of Madagascar*

The Board commissioned the building of the now famous *Adventure Galley*, for £6,000. A 287-ton ship, *Adventure* was fitted with 34 cannons and modified to increase her speed. With a crew of 80, Kidd left Plymouth in February 1696 and by August, there were eight wealthy partners reaping the benefits of Kidd's reprisals against piracy, including King William, who received 10 percent of the divided booty in an underhand deal struck with the partners. His eventual destination would be Madagascar, home of the most notorious pirates in the world, and a treacherous hive of scum and villainy.

Kidd sailed from Deptford on Feb. 27, 1696, called at Plymouth, and arrived at New York City on July 4 to take on more men. Avoiding the normal pirate haunts, he arrived by February 1697 at the Comoro Islands off East Africa. Some time after his arrival there, Kidd, still robbed of the glory of having taken a prize ship, decided to turn to piracy. In August 1697 he made an attack on ships sailing with Mocha coffee from Yemen, which proved unsuccessful, although he later captured several small ships. His crew came close to mutiny two months later, when Kidd refused to attack a Dutch ship, and in an angry exchange Kidd mortally wounded one of his crew. A most vocal member of the crew, gunner Willam Moore, had long complained about Kidd's lack of aggression. The two argued constantly about the nature of their commission - an angry exchange which finally ended in Kidd dealing a fatal blow to the man with a wooden bucket. The murder decreased Kidd's popularity among the crew and he realised that his reign as captain would

*Kidd lashes out at gunner William Moore*

soon come to an end if he did not start raiding ships and bringing in the booty. Thus he threw caution to the wind in his reckless pursuit of treasure.

His first victim was the Armenian ship "Quedagh Merchant", taken by Kidd in January 1698. It proved to be his most valuable prize, and subsequently he scuttled the "Adventure Galley", which had become unseaworthy. Reaching Anguilla, in the West Indies, in April 1699, he learned that he had been denounced as a pirate. He left the Quedagh Merchant at the island of Hispaniola and sailed in a newly purchased ship, the "Antonio", to New York City. Once there, he tried to persuade his former patron, the Earl of Bellamont, of his innocence. However, Bellamont, by then colonial governor of New York, was not convinced and sent him to England for trial

Kidd faced the court virtually defenceless, having been refused access to counsel or even a clear statement of the charges against him. Thus when the trial began, he learned to his surprise that, in addition to five counts of piracy, he also stood accused of murdering one of his crewmen. The trial according to one modern writer, 'can be viewed only as a monstrous combination of persons and events deliberately calculated to crush the blocked and frustrated Kidd.' The Captain depicted himself as torn between the conflicting necessities of controlling a riotous crew and honouring the duties of his commission.

*The missing document which proves Kidd's innocence*

Kidd testified that his men were close to mutiny by the time he reached the coast of Africa, and thus forced him to attack a fleet of 15 Mogul merchantmen. Kidd steered towards the merchant ships, but broke off the engagement and fled after finding that they were escorted by two armed Dutch ships and a Royal Navy vessel. With regards to his seizing of the *Quedah Merchant*, Kidd claimed the ship was sailing under French pass and was thus a legitimate prize under the terms of his commission. However the prosecution contested this and refused the Captain access to his papers, which he said contained a copy of the pass. Furthermore, important evidence concerning two of the piracy cases was suppressed at the trial, and some observers later questioned whether the evidence was sufficient for a guilty verdict. Nonetheless in May of 1701, Kidd was found guilty of the murder of Moore and on five indictments of piracy. He was hanged at Executioners Dock. Soon after, some of his treasure was recovered from Gardiners Island off Long Island. Proceeds from his effects and goods taken from the Antonio were donated to charity. In years that followed, the name of Captain Kidd has become inseparable from the romanticized concept of the swashbuckling pirate of Western fiction. Among other stories concerning caches of treasure he supposedly buried is Edgar Allan Poe's "The Gold Bug." After Kidd's execution by hanging on May 23rd 1701, an anonymous epitaph warned:

*Reader, near this Tomb don't stand Without some Essence in thy Hand; For here Kidd's stinking Corpse does lie, The Scent of which may thee infect. . . .*

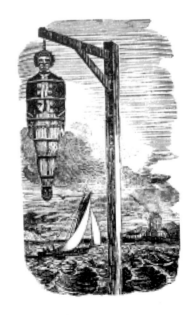

However, perhaps the most apt evaluation of Kidd's life was made by the writer Harold Thompson in 1940, when he described Kidd as 'a man neither very good nor very bad, the fool of fortune and the tool of politicians, a pirate in spite of himself'.

# CHRISSWELL

(being several verses detailing the untimely demise
of a young couple and the subsequent haunting of
their homestead)

Beyond the path, before the trees
Cresswell's blessed spring
A silence all round broken stones
And the birds won't stop to sing.

A foolish lord of Cresswell Grange
An angry prophet cross'd
He cursed the land, and cursed the well
And cursed the souls since lost.

A youth sits pale and trembling
Weeping echoes round the stone
He stole her and her heart away
But now lies empty and alone.

Her father had rejected him
Too young, too weak to wed
So wind behind them skies to guide them
The two yound lovers fled

They cross'd the river and she must
Have frowned upon their love
She clawed their boat beneath the waves
Howled the skies down from above.

They sank into the wretched dark
Death's damp dank hand took hold
But he would not let his lady die
And he dragg'd her through the cold.

Ashore. At last ashore and now
His lady cough'd and woke
And they struggl'd through the sand and dusk
And neither spectre spoke.

He hurried her into the house
Beside Christ's hallowed well
She stepped across the threshold
Cried out once and then she fell.

His lover lay down dead
And he would ever be alone
Doomed to solitude entombed
Behind decaying stone.

The cries of all the cursed
Will echo down the years
All lost and yet still wandering
By the holy well of tears.

Two lovers wander silently
Amid the rubble strewn
And celebrate perpetual love
That time may never ruin.

# Night Watch

In the 19th Century, villagers take their shift in the watchhouse
of the Innerkip Burial Committee and protect the dead from graverobbers...

Tam and Jim sat in the Burial Committee watch house and shivered.
Gravewatching was always worse in winter.

"Who is it we're lookin' oot fur the night Jim?" asked Tam.

"Dunky McDermott." said Jim.

"Dunky? Ah hated wee Dunky. Right lazy wee sod. Couldnae walk the
length o himsel'. Whit happened tae him?"

"Died in his sleep Tam."

"It's how he would o wanted it Jim." Tam shivered, "Is it no baltic the
night?"

"Absolutely. Tae be perfectly frank Tam, ah think even yer mair desperate
graverobbers are gonnae be sittin' in the night."

"At a tenner a body ah wid be oot here masel'."

"Tam!"

"Sorry Jim. Sorry. Jist shows ye that ye cannae be too careful."

Jim turned to look at Tam.

"Careful? Full moon. Sittin' in a cemetery. It's us that's askin' fur bother
really Tam. It's jist as well there's nae mair witches aboot here."

"Oh aye. Aye ah hear it wis murder wi aw the witches." nodded Tam.

"Whit wis it they used tae say Tam 'In Innerkip the witches ride thick, and
in Dunrod they dwell.' Disnae really encourage folk tae come and visit."

"Naw. Naw yer right there Jim."

"There wisnae jist witches doon oor way o' course" said Jim, assuming an
air of authority.

"Naw?"

"Naw naw, up Kilmacolm and aw roon Erskine wis hoachin' wi witches.
Hoachin'. Ye couldnae walk oot the door withoot gettin' cursed or havin'
aw pins stuck in ye."

"Really?"

"Oh aye. In fact...ma great great great grannie wis a witch."

"Yer kiddin'!"

"Not a word o a lie Tam. She wis a right nasty piece o work. Lived over
Bankfoot way. Pins widnae prick her. They'd just bust. Mind, she burned
fine right enough."

"Katy Cameron still is a witch. Her and Maggie Scott and Liz Fraser meet
up Loch Thom every full moon. And dance...nekkit."

"Aye?"

"Oh aye Jim. Me and big Wullie McPhee nipped up last month. It wis
magic. Here, ye got any o that dumplin' wi ye the night?"

"Aye...aye jist a wee bit." said Jim.

"Can ah get some."

"Eh...mebbe later. Ahm no openin' it yet."

Tam scowled.

"Anyhow," said Jim, giving himself some room "Ah wis gonnae tell ye aboot this poor chap who ran intae a few witches no aw that long ago and he fell foul of...The Enchanted Cap!"

"The whit?"

"The Enchanted Cap. That's the name o this wee story...it's aboot a sort o...magic bunnet."

Jim was a little disappointed that his story hadn't got off to quite the impressive start he was hoping for.

"Oh right. Sorry. You batter on Jim."

"Thank you. So, this guy turns up on the Greenock dock, and he's keen to get doon the road tae Largs fairly sharpish."

"Does he live in Largs Jim?"

"He does Tam. Aye. And time's knockin' on, so he figures he'll jist nip up the hill and take a short cut across the moors. Only thing is Tam...it's Halloween."

"Right."

"He's up the back, and he jist passes Dunrod Hill when this big storm starts...and it's lashin' doon. Absolutely lashin'. Thunder. Lightning. It's murder. And he's struggling along, walkin' intae the storm, when he spies this wee hut."

"Well that's a bit o luck."

"Aye Tam. It is. So he goes inside, heads up to the corner, wraps himself up in his jacket, and nods off."

"Ye sure yer no openin' that dumplin' Jim?" asked Tam, glancing hopefully at the little parcel.

"Ahm sure Tam. A few hours later, oor man gets woken up, by aw these voices...murmurin'. And there's a wee peat fire gaun in the hut. There's a pot on the fire and roon aboot it, there's three witches, muttering and incanting."

"Whit they sayin'?"

"Eh...aw sorts. Heedorum. Hodurum. Ye know the sort o thing."

"Ah do Jim."

"And the first witch right, the oldest wan, she brings oot this sorta pointy hat. She wrings it oot, as if she wis dryin' it, puts it on her head and says 'Ho! For Kintyre!' and whoosh! She goes fleein' oot the lum."

"Whit? She flies?"

"Aye. And after she's gone, the cap jist falls back down the chimney. So the second witch, sorta middle aged like, she grabs the hat, wrings it oot and shouts 'Ho! For Kintyre!' and she's away as well. The hat falls back doon, and the third witch, young, naw bad lookin', she picks it up 'Ho! For Kintyre!' and there she goes, firin' oot the chimney."

"So he's alone again?"

"He is Tam. But yer man looks oot the windae, an it's still lashin' doon.

And the cap floats back doon intae the hut and he thinks tae himsel'...ah wouldnae mind a wee go oan that hat. So he picks it up, and he says 'Ho!For Kintyre!' and..."

"How did he no jist ask tae go back tae Largs Jim?"

"That Tam, is a matter of no small curiosity. But Kintyre it wis, though I've nae doubt he regretted it, as ye'll see. So he's hurled intae space, still holding the cap, and he is speedin' through the air and he gets to Kintyre. And here, when he gets there is there no a big room full a witches. And they're aw waitin' there for the Dread Master of All Evil."

"The Devil?"

"Aye Tam. The Devil. And this year he's decided to have his big Halloween bash in the King of France's wine cellar."

"In Kintyre?"

"Again Tam, the facts o' the matter vary frae time tae time, but this much is sure, oor man ends up in Kintyre, and there's a big room fulla witches aw waitin' for the de'il tae turn up. From that ah suggest ye draw yer ane conclusions."

"Right."

"Anyhow, the witches don't seem tae mind, and he's invited tae enjoy the party. But here, he mebbe has a few wee glesses too many o the auld elderberry brew."

"So he's steamin Jim."

"He is. And he's dancin' aboot and swearin' like a loon, and the devil turns up and he has a wee dance wi him, and, well, he jist has a right good time."

"Fair do's."

"Well aye. But, he sorta comes to in the mornin' a wee bit the worse for wear, and he's in a cell in Kintyre jail. Seems he was wanderin' about the streets swearin' and smashin' things. And when he tries tae explain that it wis really aw the fault o the witches and the devil...naebody believes him."

"Aye. Ah've tried that one maself Jim."

"But he's in a right pickle, cos he's caused so much bother wi aw his swearin' and carryin' on, that he's been sentenced to hang."

"Rough night."

"It must have been. And they're aboot tae hing him, which as you can imagine, he's no aw that keen on, and so he says 'Would it be awright, if ah wore ma favourite bunnet on the gallows'."

"Ah think ah see his game Jim."

"Well aye. So they march him up to the gallows, and the big chap there, he's aboot tae put the rope roon his neck, so oor man puts the enchanted cap on and says 'Ho! For Largs!' and he's away. Jist like that."

"Lucky for him Jim."

Tam looked once again at the little parcel sitting by Jim. Jim pretended not to notice.

"Y'know, wi aw yer talkin aboot witches and spooky things Jim, it's put me in mind o a wee story ah heard maself.

"Aye?"

"Aye Jim. Concernin' Cresswell, y'know, jist across frae Dunrod farm."

"Ah know where ye are Tam."

"Well ever since that business wi' the Prophet Peden, the whole area's been cursed y'see."

"Aye. This is the chap they turned away frae the door?"

"That's the man Jim."

"And he could see the future this fella?"

"That's whit they say."

"So...ye think he'd have known he wisnae gonnae get in."

"Well ah don't know much aboot that Jim. But anyhow, after that, for a good long while, the place wis lyin' empty, naebody wanted to buy it

"Naebody likes curses Tam."

"Right enough Jim. But then, aboot a hunner years ago, this chap jist turns up. He's an ow fella. Naw very chatty. And he stays in the big hoose, all by himself."

"Nae mates?"

"Nane. And he jist gets aw his stuff delivered right tae the door. Most o the time he was pleasant enough to the folk that delivered, but every so often, they'd turn up, and he'd be shoutin' and ravin' and swearin'.
He wisnae chuffed."

"Mebbe they'd delievered the wrang stuff Tam. Forgot his totties or something."

"Mebbe Jim. Mebbe. Ah certainly widnae be too happy aboot that. But he wis loaded this auld fella. Absolutely rollin' in it. And naebody knew where aw this money had come frae. He wisnae a local business man, there was no money comin' in frae his land. But he wis still mintit."

"I wonder where aw his money came frae Tam."

"Well folk talk Jim."

"They do Tam."

"And there wis plenty folk thought that this auld man had actually been a pirate."

"Aye?"

"Oh aye Jim. In fact, wan o the boys who delivered up tae the hoose, swore blind he once came tae the door hoddin..wan o them big pirate swords."

Tam waved his arm about by way of demonstration.

"A cutlass Tam?"

"The very thing. So folk reckoned this was where aw his money came frae. Pirate gold and the like. And naturally, there was plenty folk keen tae have a wee keek inside his hoose. Jist tae see if it wis aw full o treasue chests an that."

"Ahm no sure he would have kept aw his treasure in his hoose Tam."

"Ye nivver know Jim. Anyhow, every so often, this very proper lookin'
young lady would turn up tae visit him. She'd always stay for a couple o
days and then head off again. Most folk reckoned she wis his daughter,
turnin' up tae get at him for livin' off aw these ill-gotten gains. Or mebbe
oan the bum. Either way, it wis always efter she'd been tae see him that
he'd go in the huffs."

"Sounds mair like his wife Tam."

"Could be Jim. Anyhow, here, one day, yer man dies. Jist like that. An the
first anyone knows aboot it, is that this lady turns up early one morning.
And by the evening, she's gone, and so's the auld pirates body, and all his
gold. They leave the hoose empty, and that's how it stayed for the next
hunner years."

Jim narrowed his eyes.

"A hunner. As many as that Tam?"

"Well...it wis certainly a good long while. And there's them that say Jim,
that on a crisp, clear night, ye can see him wanderin' roon the estate,
cutlass in wan hand, black flag in the other, lookin for his hoose and aw
the treasure he kept in it."

"Who says that Tam?"

"Eh...me Jim. Jist me. But wee Malkie McGhee says he saw him wan night."

"Ach Wee Malkie McGhee's got a heid fulla mince. And anyhow Tam, he
said he saw two ghosts holdin' hands. Mind, that wee couple that died no
that long ago."

"Oh aye Jim. Still. It's all go doon here. Witches. Ghosts. Graverobbers.
And of course...The Beast!"

Jim shook his head.

"Wid this be the wild howling beast of Ardgowan Tam."

"Aye. Aye. But it disnae howl...it hoots. Eerily."

Tam hooted.

"Naw Tam. That'd be an owl...owls hoot. it's maybe a right big owl. Or an
owl man."

"Jim, listen, I've been poachin' on that estate since ah wis eight year old,
ah think ah know whit an owl sounds like."

Tam cupped his hands to his mouth and hooted convincingly.

"Like that right? Too whit. Too whoo. Very simple. This...this beast...wis
something awthegither more terrifying. And it hooted."

Tam hooted once again to make his point.

"Well...ah don't know much aboot that. But ah huv heard that it's mauled
a few sheep and startled the horses."

"Aye. Apparently, all the philosophers o' The Clachan are tryin' tae figure
oot whit it is. Naebody's ever heard anythin' like it."

"Except maybe when they've heard owls."

"Naw Jim. naw. It is no a creature belonging tae this world."

"A bit like yerself in that respect Tam."

In the distance, something howled. Or hooted. And the two men shivered.

"Can ah huv a piece o that dumplin' then Jim?"

# THE BOGLE

"When the delinquent has clomb up the brae and got out of sight of the lights of the town, and was just entering the wild and dreary moor that seperates Kilmacolm from the outer world, the Bogle was frequently seen about this stone and sent the belated worthy onward at an accelerated speed, while he fancied he heard a something following at his heels.

The good wives of Kilmacolm used to say that, whether it was a ghaist or a deil it was a godsen to the kintra for it sent home Kilmacolm folks at a richt like time o nicht."

**Much About Kilmacolm 1872**

*From "Malkie and The Bogle"*
"Ye right?" asked The Bogle "Only ye've bin lyin' doon there fur aboot an hour goin' on and on aboot aw sorts a mince."
"Oh God! Aw naw! It's...you're...The Bogle!"
"Right enough." said The Bogle. "Eh...BOO!"
Malkie screamed.
"Calm it doon big yin. Ahm no gonnae batter ye."
"But...but I've been caught. By a Bogle."
"No exactly caught as such, on account of you havin' fell doon steamin' drunk. To be honest, ah didnae even see ye there, ah wis jist havin' a wee wander up the Clune Brae and ah tripped over ye, lyin' there like a big sack o' spuds wi' a bunnet."
"Aye...but..."
"And no even a very nice bunnet."
Malkie frowned.
"Is this what happens when a Bogle catches ye then? He makes wee cheeky comments aboot yer gear? Only I though somethin' terrible wis supposed tae happen, but..."
"Oh I'll no lie tae ye pal. It's no good. Yer in fur a right horrifying time o' it. All manner of eerie unearthly terrors will befall you...unless..."
"Unless..."
"Unless ye want tae try and beat me at a game or somethin'. Ahm a bit bored the night so..."
"What did ye have in mind?"
The Bogle's eyes flashed mischieviously.
"Well ah wis thinkin' mebbe...bools"

# CHRISSWELL

"Peace has a bower by still Chrisswell
But dark Dunrod conceals a witchcraft spell."

## THE HOUSE OF CHRISSWELL

In its heyday, the palace of Chrisswell was said to rival Ardgowan in size and majesty, although today it is only remembered by a small farmhouse which stands on the hill above the IBM complex.

There is mention of a chapel at Chrisswell as early as the thirteenth century, in the reign of Robert III, though a sacred well, which remains a short distance from the farmhouse, may have been in existence long before this. The waters of the well or spring, known as Boag's well, is said to have healing properties, and from this the chapel lands gained their original name of Chrystwall, or Christ's Well. In the year 1556, Sir Lawrence Galt, named as owner of the chapel grounds, deemed the lands to Sir James Lindsay, a chaplain, and his heirs; however, this right passed to the Stewart family in the late seventeenth century.

For as long as Chrisswell stood, stories of witches, ghosts and supernatural occurrences have attached themselves to the place.

## THE PROPHET PEDEN

In 1638 the Privy Council of the King, angry at the influence of Catholics over their monarch, drafted a petition demanding the removal of Bishops from the Council, a move which lead to the drawing up of the National Covenant. This document forced a wedge between the Catholic and Protestant religions and caused much civil strife throughout the country. Most noted among the Covenanters was the Prophet Peden, who is said to have famously cursed Chrisswell in the seventeenth century, during the Scottish civil war.

Hunted by Catholics for much of his life, Peden often took refuge in the hills around Spango Glen. One night however, when the weather was particularly harsh, he sought admittance at Chrisswell farm. At this time the house was occupied by one Monteith, a direct descendant of the Monteith who betrayed William Wallace, and a fierce opponent of the Covenanters. Peden was refused admittance and took out his wrath on the inhabitants, declaring that for their unkindness, the traffic of the world would one day pass through their midst and that the roof would be open to the winds of heaven. It is strange to note that with the construction of the IBM factory and a well travelled dual carriageway passing through the former grounds of Chrisswell, it would appear as if some, if not all of Peden's prophecy has been fulfilled.

## GHOSTS & LEGENDS

The years following Peden's Curse are replete with tales and legends of a dark nature. One tradition has it that the knoll at the back of the house was a rendezvous for the notorious Renfrewshire Witches, and on more than one occasion, the "diabolical hell broth" was brewed there under the direct supervision of Satan himself.

Another grisly tale tells of a drummer boy, returning home from war long ago. It was a dark winter's eve, as the legend has it, and the witches were abroad. Eager for a young sacrifice for one of their dark rituals, one of the hags transformed herself into a wolf, tearing the innocent young boy to pieces.

*Inverkip Graveyard*

Yet another legend recalls that the house was inhabited by a pirate who, having acquired a mass of wealth in Madagascar and the West Indies, came home to seek in retirement that peace which repentance alone can give. He was a grey haired, hard featured, solitary man. A lady, a stranger, visited him at rare intervals; this generally made him moodier. After his death, it was frequently said that his ghost was observed, cutlass in one hand, black flag in the other, stalking on moonlit nights amid the ruins.

Others say that the last proprietor of Chrisswell was a gentleman who had been unhappy in some love affair. He had eloped with a fair haired lady from her guardian's house and was proceeding homeward to his residence in Inverkip Glen. The boat crossing from Bute to the mainland was upset, and the bride and groom barely escaped with their lives. Soon after reaching her new home, the young lady sank and died in his arms. Her inconsolable husband lived the life of a recluse, dying at an early age of a broken heart. Two figures clothed in snowy raiment have been seen gliding hand in hand about the ruin.

*A gravestone in Inverkip Graveyard*

## THE GRAVEWATCHERS

Towards the end of the 18th Century in Inverkip, there began a series of graveyard robberies committed by a body of men who became known as The Resurrectionists. Undisturbed by any feeling of respect for the dead - more concerned with the £10 per body bounty they claimed on their poor late victims - they went about their gruesome business. Frequently the body would be lifted and taken away on the same day as interment.

Societies sprung up everywhere to guard the sanctity and peace of the grave. In 1828 the Innerkip Burial Committee was formed. It was the duty of its members to appoint a watch every night after a burial. A watch house was built for this purpose.

It was during this time that Inverkip suffered a spate of frequent hauntings, many of which were centred around the hallowed grounds of the churchyard. In 1837, for several weeks, locals were disturbed by strange unearthly sounds. Villagers attested to hearing 'many a howlet cry, but sic anither cry as this ane they nivir heard before', and could not allow themselves to believe it came from an earthly creature; the gamekeeper of nearby Ardgowan, however, asserted plausibly that it was a peculiar species of owl.

# The Legacy
# of Para Handy

*"We went into Greenock for some marmalade...*
*and did we no stay for three days."*

Master Mariner Para Handy is perhaps the most famous folk hero associated with Inverclyde, having been immortalised in print, on stage and on screen. Created by Inverary born Neil Munro, the stories of Para Handy and the Vital Spark provide a vivid and enduring snapshot of "a golden age" along the Firth of Clyde and in amongst its ports and villages. Munro was a journalist by trade and although tales of Para Handy, Dougie and the rest are most noted for their sublime comic stylings, they often contained gentle social comment and occasionally satirised topical events.

The Para Handy stories first appeared in the Glasgow Evening News in 1905, and to this day there remains little to match this evocative comic Scots prose. It is of course the various television incarnations which people are most familiar with, and which provide Inverclyde's most direct link with the Master Mariner. Much of the filming for the BBC television series of the seventies was done in and around Greenock. Indeed it was here that the puffer "The Vital Spark" was berthed for a good many years. However the poor puffer met a rather ingracious end at the hands of some forward thinking local officials...

# The Day They Sank The Vital Spark

The Vital Spark and her sister ship were both berthed over in Bowling right? And that's really where the mystery starts, 'cos there's naebody aw that sure which wan o' the two o' them it wis came over tae Greenock. Ah say it wis The Vital Spark right enough, or at least, it wis the wan they used on the telly. Anyhow, the two steamers, are sittin' in this mud over in Bowling, and somebody over oor end thinks 'hing on, this wee ship could make a right nice wee tourist attraction'. Which is fair enough. But it turns oot it's in a bit o' a state, so it gets hauled doon tae Adams yard in Gourock tae be repaired.

Then Adams yard gets shut. So they decide tae move it up tae Lamonts dry dock, which at the time is actually a wet dock. And they stick it in there, and that's where it sits while they decide whit tae dae wi' it.

So all of a sudden, there's a lot mair space up that end o' the toon, and the big idea is tae build a 'maritime heritage centre'. They've got wan doon in Troon. Huv ye been? It's naw bad.

Anyhow, this crowd called 'Inverclyde Initiative' commission a 'feasability

study' on whether or no' we should build this centre commemorating oor heritage, geneaology and proud shipbuilding past, and they decide instead tae build a few big empty buildings.

But in amongst aw this, the poor Vital Spark's jist sittin' there in Lamonts, and she's no gettin' any better. Fallin' tae pieces is mair like it. So wan o these naw so vital bright sparks, gets it intae his heid that they need tae preserve the puffer while they decided whit they're daein'. And he's heard that the salt water will preserve the boat, so he says jist sink it intae the dry dock. We suggested that maybe this wisnae such a great idea, and he said jist tae dae it anyhow. And I very politely declined and me and Malkie went aff fur a wee spot o' lunch.

When we  gets back, they're half roads through sinking it. I couldnae believe it.

We once again very politely suggested that they take a moment to reconsider their actions. And they told us tae shut it.

So they sink the Vital Spark intae the dock and leave it there. So surprise surprise, it rusts tae bits. And we told them, if Malkie wis here he would tell ye. Nae vision. That's whit it's like but. Murder. Utter murder.

It's a wee piece o' oor history ye know? Somethin' folk could have enjoyed. I mean, awright, it wis never gonnae be sailin' again, but then, ye cannae sail up and doon the clyde in a big yella kettle either. Whitever next? They'll be shuttin' off the river at the Erskine bridge end and bannin' ice cream on The Esplanade.

Honestly. Jist as well we've still got The Comet. If we keep gettin' rid o' aw this stuff there'll be nothin' left fur the tourist information office tae tell folk. And whit then eh?

Ahm away, these midgies are eatin' me alive.

# CROW MOUNT

From "Views & Reminiscences of Old Greenock" James McKelvie & Sons 1891

"This picture is interesting as taking us back some fifty years in the history of Greenock. Crow Mount, or, as it was commonly called, the Mount, formed that portion of the town stretching westwards from Bank Street to Ann Street, and running northwards from Dempster Street to Roxburgh Street. The district represented by the Mount is now covered with dwellings. Crow Mount was in its way, a miniature forest, with trees of luxuriant growth, which attracted crows, and made it a breeding place and a centre for this well known species of bird, the chorus of whose peculiar cawing became a familiar feature of the neighbourhood and doubtless gave the Mount its name. The pictorial sketch herewith is in striking contrast to the transformation which exists today and is significantly suggestive as to how Greenock in her later years, has outgrown her original boundaries and extended herself into the country."

She does not walk the path,
The crone,
But wanders down from
The hills like mist
And moves silently
Between the trees
On the mount.

Rolled in a rag
Are the bones
She'll cast
To summon Morrigan;
Mother-of-war.
Crow-witch.
The carrion queen.

Badb, Macha, Neman.
Three of one,
All called
To halt the advance
Of cobble grey legions
That storm the green
With sandstone and smoke.

Badb is
The washer at the stone.
The blood of the nearly dead
Runs red from the
Torn chainmail of
Those who will fall.
Do not see her.

Macha, blood beaked,
Battle borne
On wing and claw.
She rips into the fray
And tears away the souls
Of the unjust.
Do not fear her.

Neman, howling
Mother mourns
Her fallen sons.
The sing song shriek
Of the carrion chorus
Sounds once and is gone.
Do not hear her.

The mount echoes
With the moans
Of old ghosts,
And the sky blackens
One bird at a time.
Sorrow. Joy. Silver. Gold.
She comes.

The Morrigan's judgement
Is her own.
She will not wrench
The town to pieces
Nor drench it
In fire and blood.
She sees the battle lost.

The old gods
Have flown.
The hag, gathers her bones
In her rag and scowls down.
Seven crows circle. A secret.
Slowly the town
Washes back from the river.

# The Mysterious Mystery of The Lang House Ghost

*A self-proclaimed hunter of all things dark and spectral*
*seeks out a new adventure with the help of his stout companion,*
*and gains more than he bargained for...*

Being an adventure featuring the Remarkable and Notable Mister James John L_____ of Greenock (Erstwhile Ghost Hunter), and his Hardy Compatriot, Andrew 'Sandy' Mc_____.

## 1: I decide on my mission

Many have spoke ill of me, all the years of my life. I have been referred to behind cupped hands and raised newspapers as indolent and slothful; these words do not hurt me. It has been said that I an content to rest my laurels here at M_____ House, letting my poor late father's money and interests work for me, never once paying a visit to the factories and retailers which keep me in the manner which I have not earned; the haughty looks bother me not. I see the way part before me wherever I go, when all I wish is to mix with the people of this town, walking where they walk. Even so, I remain unperturbed, not because I am the ignorant fop I am proclaimed to be, but because I have been witness over these past few days to sights which have blinded me to all else in my life. Sights which have me doubting everything but the evidence of my two good eyes.

There. That's gotten all of the soul-searching mumbo-jumbo out of the way; perhaps, now, I can begin to tell you of the events which brought me to the Lang House, and what I saw there.
I had heard of the house, of course; a remarkable, imposing, turreted structure clearly visible from the road running to the Daff Glen, it tends to stand out somewhat from the surrounding trees. Still, never would I have given it a second thought, had I not begun to hear whispering and murmurings of ghostly shenanigans within the walls of the great house.

Those of you who have chanced to read my earlier forays into the world of the othernormal - **The Strange Case of the Man With No Plan in Life** in particular was considered for publication in no less a periodical than The Strand Magazine - will be well aware of my long-standing fascination with spookly matters and such. As you can imagine, my nose was veritably twitching at the possibilities.

I ventured an enquiry or three in the right avenues and was rewarded with very little; strangely enough, very few people seem to have any firsthand knowledge of who has ever dwelled in the great house, let alone any tragedy which may have befallen them to cause their souls to wander there still. I finally got a little closer to the truth when I ran into Jock 'Jock' Scott, sometime resident of the _____ _____ Public Bar, propping up the

wood in said establishment.

"Ghostses it is," intoned Jock in plummy tones, his nose almost in his ale. He was three sheets to the wind by this time, which was to be expected; after all, it was past three in the afternoon. "Ghostses, roamin' aw ower the blummin' place. Goin like this. Wooooooo."

"Yes, Jock, I know that," said I, patiently. I had a great deal of time for Jock; he had been of great help to myself and Sandy in *The Dastardly Case of the French Sailors Haunting the Cemetery* (I've never liked that title. Still; too late now), keeping a midnight watch with us three nights running until we saw the ghastly apparitions, weaving out of the fog, stinking of the nether world and singing 'La Marseillaise' in close harmony. Dreadful. Dreadful business. "What I need to know, Jock my dear fellow, is who they are. Why are they haunting the Lang House? What keeps them there?"

At this, he fixed his one good eye on me - the other seemed to be fixed on his own right ear - and drew in breath in a long wheezing inward cough which quite worried me.

"Terrible thing. Poor wee lassie. Lovely she wis. Lovely. Died. Died she did. Broken herted. There wis a fella, awa' fightin' in the war. And there wis anither fella. Don't know who he wis. There wis love, an' fightin', and she died. Terrible thing."

This momentous speech over, Jock focused the steady half of his vision on his glass, and I would get no more sense out of him on this night.

Still; I had a little information in hand. I had embarked on ghost hunts with far less. I would speak to a ghost, or I would die in the attempt. Well. Bit drastic, there, but you understand.

## 2: I recruit my partner in ghost-hunting

Sandy seemed unenthusiastic for a yomp into the world of the supernatural, which surprised me, considering his standing as my hale and hearty compatriot on countless (well, 9) earlier adventures.

Granted, it was 1:23 in the hours of the morning and, also granted, I had turned up unannounced at his door in stout walking boots and carrying a bulky pack of essentials ( I had left my blunderbuss at home only after great deliberation). Also, regrettably, Sandy was still recovering from a recently broken arm. Even so, though, I feel I deserved a warmer reception than my old friend gave me.

"Whit? Whit's your game, Jimmy? D'ye know whit time it is? In the name o' God, Jimmy. Whit?"

Unfazed by this drowsy outburst, I pressed on with the case at hand, explaining that time was of the essence; no self-respecting spectre would walk the halls of his (her) former home by the hours of daylight.

"Well, whit's wrang wi' tomorra night, ya numpty-heid?" Sandy was beginning to bog me down with his belligerence, he really was.

"Tomorrow night? Tomorrow night? Can this be the Andrew 'Sandy' Mc_____ I know so well? I remember the time when you'd have jumped at the chance to aid me in the study of a ghostly apparition! Jumped, I say!"

"Aye. Well. That's as may be. Ye might have noticed ma arm's broke. Ye might also have noticed this wee note on ma arm-cast here." He pointed to a patch of plaster, but I confess in the dim lamplight I was unable to see it. I leaned forward, squinting. "What does it say?"

"YOUR FAULT!" Sandy's cry caused me to step back, blinking in mute disbelief. "Your fault, ya puddin'! 'Gi'es a hand at the cinema, Sandy, this ghost's a right bugger tae catch.' 'Aye, nae bother, Jimmy - aw, no, he's awa' and broke ma arm."

"Sandy, now, I have time and again apologised for the events at the culmination of **The Mystery of the Cinema Ghost**. I didn't expect the ghost to become corporeal."

Sandy raised his bushy eyebrows at this. "Aye, Jimmy, funny enough, that's jist whit Ah thought when the big bugger wis breakin' ma arm. 'Funny that, Ah didnae expect him tae become corporeal.'"

There was a silence, during which we stole furtive awkward glances at each other in the dim light.

I cannot remember who began to laugh first. Still, in the next few moments, we were guffawing loudly, tears rolling down my cheeks, Sandy roaring with gales of laughter, temporarily unmindful of his injury, and we were fast friends again. The cackling dried, tailed off, and Sandy looked out at me over his reading glasses.

"Will ye help me lace up ma walkin' boots?"

Forty-five minutes later (helping a man who is basically one-armed to dress is not pleasant; I do not urge you to try it at any time) we were away, and I hoisted the pack up onto my back, holding the door for Sandy to squeeze past me. He caught sight of the grappling hooks poking from the bag's mouth, and raised his eyebrows in a silent question in my direction.

"In case we have to go in over the roof, my dear chap."

Sandy shook his sizeable head. "In the name o' God," he said in a murmur.

## 3: The mission proper

In the end, the grapples were not necessary; the house, abandoned now for a number of years I was not aware of, had been left unmanned, unwatched, unlocked. Our spirits (no pun intended) truly heartened by this turn of events, even Sandy seemed bolstered and keen for action as we made our way through the midnight rooms and shadow-lengthened corridors, a lantern giving us low illumination, for even an amateur ghost-grabber like myself knows that wandering spirits hate strong light.

For that reason, both of us are surprised when we see the light.

A pinpoint at first, moving slowly along the floor of the grand dining room, Sandy and I dutifully if nervously follow it as it grows; bright as a lantern; bright as summer daylight in a darkened room; finally growing too bright for our eyes, swelling in size, a ball of purest white six feet across.
"Jimmy, Ah'm feelin' thon feelin' Ah got jist before Ah got ma arm broke."
"Take heart, old friend. I feel no malice from this entity. It seems benign."
"Och, well, that's awright then. Batter on." Sandy's sarcasm, I feel, often brings a touch of humour to our adventures. I sometimes lead him to believe that this is the reason I bring him along on my adventures; lucky for us that we both know better.

My lantern flickers and dies, but no matter; the room is as bright as day now, glowing from within because of this heavenly ball of light which even now has shapes, grey and dancing, flickering within it. The very air seems changed; the hairs on my body stand on end in quite unattractive fashion, and I fear to look at Sandy for fear of what this phenomenon has done to his splendid moustache.

Despite Sandy's exhortations to "Keep back, ya middenheid!" I slowly make my way forward toward the angelic luminosity, keeping my empty hands in front of me, supplicating myself to this shade, whoever it may once have been.

With a sound like a hundred people drawing in breath at once, the grey shapes suddenly coalesce, forming into the shape of - a girl.
Here it is my turn to draw in sharp breath, for *what* a girl! Chimneyfire hair streaming over her shoulders, large soulful eyes - and soft, full lips that could draw stories from a mute. My mission is temporarily forgotten as this vision in plain silk blouse and dark velvet skirt faces me, and smiles.
"She better no brek ma ither arm, Jimmy," comes to me from a distance. Sandy's voice is lost to me; it seems as though this maiden's ball of light swells to encompass me, drawing me closer to her. Her eyes are kind, and I can see only her as her hand reaches, reaches, finger pointing, and touches the back of my hand. Just once.

*Duncan where is my Duncan gone in the war and William where is my William gone by someone's hand though not mine I swear not mine they call me the worst of names harlot strumpet worse worse worse and I cry though what good does it they seek to hunt me out I am sure they think poor William was my fault he was only a good soul who showed a lonely girl some kindness I would never have betrayed my Duncan he was my heart and my treasure but there was someone else I could not see a face*

there was a flash and a cry and William lay dead and all I could do was
cradle his kind head in my hands as the life leaked out of him and oh, me,
oh, me, what will happen now
Duncan where is my Duncan lost in the war and William where is my
William gone by someone's hand though not mine both my fine men dead
now dead now and I will find them I have spent every night since that
night I gave up and used my own two good hands to join them in Heaven
but I cannot find them where are they tell me where my Duncan my William
my two fine men

This tirade, soft and entreating, is in my head in an instant, her nightly
prayer since she took her own life, and there are tears rolling down my
cheeks as I understand her.

The procedure for 'exorcising' a spirit, for sending it on its way to the
other side, is long, and drawn out, and sometimes very unpleasant for all
concerned.

The smile she gives me when she fades into darkness, the sigh she
expounds as she gives herself over, is more than enough reward.

The dawn has come an hour hence when we make our weary way out of
the stout doors of the Lang House. I clap Sandy, stout fellow that he is, on
the shoulder, and thank him once again for his help in a thankless task. In
the early light I can see tears brimming in his eyes.
"Will......will she be awright noo, Jimmy? Aye?"
I smile, my grip on Sandy's shoulder tightening for a moment, and my
voice, too, is thick with emotion.
"She will, Sandy, old man. I know it."
We walk down the gravel path, taking our time, enjoying what will be
another lovely day.

There you have it; what I am reasonably sure will be my last case. I grow
too old to be chasing after spooks and spectres in all hours of the night,
sending them on their way with a flea in their ear, or a blessing.
Then again, you never know what kind of trouble will seek out an amateur
ghost hunter. Perhaps Mister James John L_____ of Greenock (Erstwhile
Ghost Hunter), and his Hardy Compatriot, Andrew 'Sandy' Mc_____ will
return in another adventure which is both breathtaking and enlightening.

Sandy's arm is healing up nicely, by the way.

# HAUNTINGS

Inverclyde, like any area, has gathered several prominent ghosts in its history, tales of which still pass from hand to mouth down the generations.

*The Lang House*

### THE LANG HOUSE GHOST

Stories differ as to the identity of this spectre, but but the tale which passed into our hands tells of a young woman who, with her husband at war (again, which war he fought in is a lost detail), sought innocent comfort with a male friend. This friendship was looked on with suspicious eyes by locals, who came to the Lang House one night to drag the unfortunate man away and hang him from the high branches of a birch tree. The poor young woman received word the very next day of her husband's death in combat and, overcome by grief, she took her own life. It is said her shade still walks the halls of the Lang House seeking out the lost men of her life.

### THE WHITE LADY OF CASTLE LEVAN

Lady Marion Mongomery was a former keeper of the castle who was convicted of the vicious torture and murder of her tenants and sentenced to death by the mother of Mary Queen of Scots, Mary of Guise. This sentence, however, was commuted, and instead Marion was put under house arrest for the rest of her days. Not that she had gotten off lightly; Marion's husband returned from military service to discover the tragic story of his wife's crimes and he imprisoned her, starving her to death.

In later years, during the 17th century, the first sightings of a 'white lady' were reported. At the time, the castle was owned by the Semple-Stewarts of the

*Castle Levan*

nearby Ardgowan estate; the family had housed their young son there. Indeed, some believe that the story of the 'white lady' was invented by the young Semple-Stewart in an effort to persuade his wealthy father to purchase him a new house instead of lodging him in an ancient castle.

Many other tales still survive to this day of hauntings and apparitions in and around the area: the spectral French sailors reputed to haunt Greenock Cemetary, the ghost who haunted the old Odeon Cinema and, most recently, an exorcism carried out in a council flat, also in Greenock - front page local news at the time.

# Restoration

*In the midst of the Greenock Blitz, a young boy has a magical encounter*
*with three strange characters...*

Jamie had been dreaming about pirates when his mother dragged him from his bed. Together they ran to the moorland up behind the houses, the sirens howling all the while.

"Oh God! That wis Bawhirley Road."

Below, the streets flashed and flared with violent light, the cries of the gathered children echoing through the dark. Tonight, the bombs fell not only across the town, but onto the surrounding hills.

"We should have ran to the railway tunnels."

"Ach it's aw wan Mary. There's naewhere safe the night."

Mary shrugged and then gestured down to the distillery fire still snaking through the streets.

"Would ye look at that fire. Aw that whisky."

"Aye. There's plenty would be swimmin' in it if it wisnae fur aw they flames."

Jamie wandered back over to where his mother was sitting with the baby.

"Mammy."

His mother was busy comforting wee Anna.

"Mammy. I've got tae go."

"Can ye naw hod it in?"

"I'll explode!"

"Oh fur goodness sake. Away over tae those trees well."

Jamie was off and running.

"Don't you go far."

He was already gone.

Jamie peered through the trees out onto the endless black.

Nothing, nothing at all...except...except a little cottage. A candle flickered in the window.

Jamie glanced back towards his mother and the others.

"Ach. They wint even notice ahm gone."

And so, rather than waste valuable time arguing with himself, Jamie ran carefully towards the cottage.

There was a dragon carved into the dark wooden door, and right in the centre, was a brass doorknocker shaped like a gargoyle.

Jamie knocked.

"Come in." said a little old voice.

And he did. Inside, a little old man was packing a large selection of colourful hats into a large wooden chest. The chest was almost full and there were still many hats scattered all around the floor. A few of them appeared to be moving. The Old Man turned to face him.

"Oh. Hello."

"Hullo." said Jamie, and then, unsure of what to say next, he added, "Ah like yer door."

"Hmmm? Oh the serpent? Yes it's nice. Although I sometimes think the gargoyle might be overdoing it slightly."

Jamie shrugged.

"Are ye okay in here?"

The Old Man looked around the interior of the cottage as if assessing any impending emergencies.

"Absolutely. Why, is something wrong?"

"Well...wi the bombs..."

"Ah yes the bombs." said the Old Man. "And the fire. No I'm fine thank you young man."

Jamie stared for a moment.

"That is some beard you've got mister."

"Yes." said the Old Man, self consciously fingering his voluminous beard. "I've let it go a bit of late but..."

He removed a little twig.

"...oh dear. How embarassing."

"I'm Jamie by the way."

"I did not ask for your name young man, and in future I suggest you be more careful who you give it to."

"Ye whit?"

Merlin sighed.

"Hello Jamie. I'm Merlin. I probably shouldn't tell you that, but I doubt it really matters."

"Merlin? The wizard?"

"Yes. Merlin the wizard."

"Right 'en."

"What? You don't believe me?"

"Naw." said Jamie "Naw really. Tae me ye jist look like some ow guy livin' in a doo hut."

Merlin looked around his cottage once again. Jamie did have a point. He really should have a bit of a tidy up sometime.

"Dae a trick." suggested Jamie.

"Do a..? Young man I am not about to justify my ancient magical heritage by pulling a rabbit out of a hat. Although I am tempted to saw you in half."

Jamie stared, unimpressed.

"Oh for heaven's sake." scowled Merlin, reaching behind Jamie's ear. "What's this?"

He produced a coin.

"Half a crown?" suggested Jamie hopefully.

"No." said Merlin. "It is a coin cast in the sixth century. It commemorates

the Battle of Arderryd."

Merlin held the coin between thumb and forefinger. Suddenly, it burst into a bright green flame, and in the fire, Jamie could see the battle raging. Just as suddenly, the flame flickered and died.

"Everything changes," said Merlin, rather pleased that Jamie was finally interested.

"So you really ur Merlin? Like wi King Arthur and aw that?"

"It's always Arthur isn't it? I've been around for well over fifteen hundred years, and I spent less than eighty of them with him!"

"Ye met him? Ye really met him and aw the Knights like in the serials? What was he like?"

"Shorter than you would imagine," said Merlin.

"Waste of space if you ask me," said a voice from the shadows.

"Well nobody did ask you." said Merlin rather testily.

A little man stepped out into the light the fire cast across the room.

"Here, has that fella got wee horns?"

"All the better to butt you with," smiled the Little Man.

"Oh d'ye think so?"

Merlin shuffled diplomatically towards Jamie, placing himself between he and the fireplace.

"Please allow me to introduce...The Great God Pan!"

Pan played a little tune on his pipes by way of introduction.

"Aye. Hullo."

Unhappy with this chilly reception, Pan scowled and shivered in an exaggerated fashion.

"It's freezing in here Merlin."

Merlin looked at Jamie and gestured to the door.

"Well are you in or out."

Beyond the trees, the bombs kept falling.

"In. Thanks," replied Jamie, turning to shut the door. It was already closed.

"Tea?" asked Merlin. "Or coffee...although we've only got that dreadful hickory stuff. Personally I think it tastes like pig pee but Pan swears by it."

Pan grinned and raised his bottle of Camp in silent salute.

"Although to be fair," pondered Merlin "Pan swears by most things."

"Whit ye aw daein here?" asked Jamie.

"We've popped round to see an old chum."

Merlin pointed to the furthest away corner of the room where a slouched shape sat, rocking gently back and forth, holding a shell to his ear. Every so often, he would nod and smile, as if agreeing with the empty whistling song of the sea.

"He hasn't been feeling very well," said Merlin. "So we've been trying to convince him to come on a little holiday with us."

Pan emptied a rabbit from one of Merlin's hats, grabbing it merrily by the ears.

"Put that down Pan. You don't know where it's been."

"No," he smiled "But I know where it's going."

Merlin tutted.

"He went out with Bacchus a week ago last Tuesday. He's been insufferable since."

"So...you're Merlin aye? And that's Pan." Jamie turned to the corner. "So, who are you?"

The figure straightened himself up and brushed down his rags in a haphazard attempt to appear dignified.

"I am Lorne of the Trees. Spirit of this Land."

This display seemed to tire him and Lorne slumped back into the corner, once again cradling the seashell to his ear.

"Naw very chatty is he?"

"He's depressed," said Pan. "He wants to get out more."

"He's lost his ladyfriend," explained Merlin.

"Oh, right," said Jamie "Is she pretty?"

"Well, mainly she's a sort of a...sea monster."

"A monster?"

"A really nice one though. Her name's Clutha."

"When did he last see her?" Jamie asked

"Ehm...when the earth was still young wasn't it Lorne?"

Lorne nodded miserably.

"Ages ago," said Merlin. "Literally."

"Grannu would not let our love flourish. I was tied to the land, and she was bound to the seas."

"Yes well he's always been a bit moody has Grannu," explained Merlin.

"No sense of humour," mused Pan, absent mindedly stroking a little scar above his right eye. "Marvellous singing voice though."

Jamie turned once more to face Lorne.

"Where's Clutha now?"

"The river."

"Whit? That yin doon there? She lives in the Clyde?"

"She is the Clyde."

Jamie turned to Merlin.

"Please young man, don't expect me to explain the physics of myth and metaphor to you. I don't even try to understand it myself."

"And I," said Pan proudly "can't even say it."

Jamie frowned.

"So...yer in love wi the river, but yer no allowed tae go anywhere near it...her?"

"Not for centuries." replied Lorne.

"And, huv ye been this doon in the dumps aw that time?"

Lorne shook his head, and a few dead leaves floated gently towards the floor.

"Don't worry," said Merlin, producing a little dustpan and brush "I'll eh...I'll get those."

"I have always been sad that I cannot see her. But across the years, there has been much else to occupy me. It is only now, as I near the end of my time, that I realise how much I want to be with her."

"You're being melodramatic Lorne," said Merlin "It's hardly 'the end of your time'."

"Then why are you trying to convince me to leave?"

"Well...uhm..." explained Merlin.

"This is my land. I do not want to leave it. But...I am...alone."

"Oh come on!" said Pan "Merlin and me are here. And young ehm...little.."

"Jamie."

"Jamie. He's here. I'll crack open the spam and we'll have a right laugh!"

Jamie ignored Pan, once more turning his attention to Lorne.

"If yer this lonely...how de ye no jist go an' talk tae her?"

"NO!" exclaimed Merlin. "Sorry. Ahem. I mean...no. He can't. Lorne and Clutha were separated by the oldest of the old gods."

Merlin shot Jamie a very sharp look.

"Right. Okay, so ye cannae talk tae her. But that disnae mean ye huvtae go away. I mean, is there naebody else roon here ye can talk tae?"

Lorne thought for a moment.

"There is a hag lives out Lochwinnoch way, we sit sometimes, and discuss the old ways and days. But she forgets things. And so there is only me to remember them."

"A hag? Whit de ye mean, a witch like?"

"Yes. She has been doing her best to bring down the planes from the hilltops. But she is old and the climb is hard. "

"She's bringing doon the jerries wi magic?"

Lorne looked momentarily sheepish.

"She shows no mercy to any of the planes."

"Whit?!"

Merlin stepped in to calm the waters once again.

"Don't worry though...she's rubbish."

"Yes," agreed Lorne "Her skills fade with every passing season."

"Oh come on Lorne! She was always rubbish" said Pan.

"It's because we forget. She forgets. Magic is less potent now."

"Oh really?" asked Merlin, delving into one of his many hats in an impressive fashion. After a few embarassed moments of frantically searching around

inside, he set it down quietly and glared at Pan.

"Sorry Merlin." said Pan "I eh...I had to borrow the rabbit out of that one."

"There wasn't a rabbit *in* that one," said Merlin "That was the one with the baby Gryphon."

"Hmmm. It *was* a trifle gamey for rabbit," nodded Pan.

"Would you just stop touching my stuff!" exclaimed Merlin angrily.

Jamie sat shaking his head, still rather annoyed by the behaviour of the Lochwinnoch witch.

"Ah cannae believe she's makin' the planes crash. Whit's she daein that fur?"

"When it was not the planes it was the ploughs, when it was not the ploughs, it was the motorcars or the engines in the factories," explained Lorne, "She does not like machines."

"How naw?" asked Jamie.

"The machines remove the need for magic."

"Oh I don't know," said Merlin "Some of the actual machines themselves are pretty magic. Planes are great. In my day, if you wanted to fly anywhere it meant spending all week being terribly pleasant to a witch."

Lorne remained unconvinced.

"This war. These times. It marks the final end of our kind. Nothing can be the same."

"Nothings ever the same though," said Pan "That's half the fun of it all."

"Exactly!" said Merlin "I remember when all the saints turned up with their new religion, and everyone was moaning about the end of the old ways. And yet here we are now, centuries later. *Still* moaning. Lorne, the machines will come and eventually, they will go, and then *these* times will seem as unreal as the last grand days of Atlantis. The skies will shift, the lands will rise and fall and once again, whole cities will sink into the sea. People, faces, places will all change, but the stories...the stories will remain. *Imagination* is the key to our hidden world, and that is where we will always be. Waiting."

Lorne nodded.

"I will come. But not until I have heard news of Clutha."

"Lorne..."

"I've been seeking consultation with the Mermaid Oracle at Port Glasgow."

"Irene? How's she doing?" asked Pan.

"All the better from being nowhere near you I imagine," replied Merlin "Poor woman."

"She didn't see *me* coming," grinned Pan.

Lorne ignored this lascivious outburst, and continued.

"She will tell me how Clutha fares. It has been so long since I last heard of her."

"Well  she was fine the last time I saw her," said Pan.

"And when was that exactly?" asked Merlin.

"Ehm...after that do on Dumbarton rock. Somebody's funeral I think."

"Oh yes," said Merlin "It was one of mine, well, Lailoken's. I'd taken a bit of a funny turn. Lights in the sky, portents of doom. All that sort of thing."

"It was probably that elderberry homebrew of Herne's. That stuff would take your head right off, I woke up in Syria."

A hollow whisper echoed around the little room, the Oracle's song.

Lorne held out the seashell.

"The oracle wishes to speak. Excuse me."

Lorne hurried back off into the corner. Pan coughed absent mindedly and then lunged melodramtically towards Jamie.

"Banana?" said Pan, producing an enormous bunch of them from behind Jamie's ear.

"Bananas! You've got bananas?"

"Yes," grinned Pan "And I understand that you...have *no* bananas. What with the war and all that."

Merlin smacked Pan gently across the back of his head.

"They have no bananas Pan, because you keep stealing them all."

"Yes. Because it's funny."

"It wasn't so funny when that whopping great tarantula was hiding in one of the crates."

Pan's face darkened.

"Yes," he agreed "That was not funny."

"And it took over the scullery and we couldn't get to the fruitloaf."

"Mmmm."

"And we had to get Thor round to kill it. So embarassing."

Lorne reappeared from the corner of the cottage, and silently placed the seashell on the shelf above the fireplace.

"So how's the good lady?" smiled Pan, nudging Lorne suggestively. "Full of herring swimming free?"

"She's dying," said Lorne.

For a moment, the cottage was silent and still, Merlin and Pan glanced awkwardly at one another.

"I should go to her."

"You know you can't do that," said Merlin gently. "Grannu wouldn't be best pleased. Even now."

Lorne hung his head.

"Can ye naw jist nip doon fur a wee minute?" asked Jamie.

"No," said Merlin firmly, "He can't."

"But she's gonny die!"

"That is how things are," said Lorne "Merlin is right. It is her time. And

mine too."

"Finally!" said Merlin "So, will you join us?"

Lorne opened the carved wooden door and walked out into the daybreak. Merlin, Pan and Jamie followed.

"I will," said Lorne "But first I wish to run across my hills and moors one last time."

Merlin nodded.

"Certainly. Take as long as you like."

Lorne smiled.

"And there is one final matter to be dealt with," he said, turning to face Jamie.

"Jamie. Can you do something for me?"

"Aye. How? Whit dae ye want me tae dae?"

Lorne reached into his rags, and removed an acorn made of gold.

"I was given this gift a very long time ago Jamie. I want you to return it for me."

Lorne handed the little acorn to Jamie, it was warm and heavy, and it shone in the first of the early morning sun.

"When you leave the moor, walk carefully down through the town to the waters edge, and throw the acorn as far into the river as you can. She will know I have not forgotten her. Can you do that for me?"

"Aye. Aye course."

Lorne placed his mossy hand upon Jamie's shoulder.

"Thank you."

"We'll just wait here then?" said Merlin.

"Yes. I will be back presently," said Lorne "I'm not going too far."

Pan and Merlin watched Lorne wander off into the forest, and saw a large black cat run off across the moorland and out of view. The two stood silently for a moment, and then Pan coughed.

"You do realise he's never coming back," he said.

"Not to us. No," said Merlin, "*He's* not going anywhere."

"Well," mused Pan, swigging another bottle of Camp "No one could say we didn't try."

"Well exactly," said Merlin.

"And if anyone *does* say that, I'll flatten them."

Jamie stared into the distance smiling.

"That wis magic," he said "He jist ran away frae ye. Jist so he could stay here."

"Yes. Well, " said Merlin. "That's his decision. We on the other hand, must be going."

"Yup," said Pan. "Nice to have met you Jamie. Enjoy the bananas."

"Yes," said Merlin "And remember not to forget. Like uhm...elephants.

Yes. Elephants."

Even as they spoke, they grew fainter, until both they and the cottage had disappeared and Jamie stood alone on the moorland. Grabbing his bananas, he began the walk back.

The sun was rising over the broken bones of the town, twisted metal and fractured stone scattered sullenly across the memory of yesterdays streets. In one night, the geography of the town was entirely altered, and there was no map. Streets disappeared, or became little islets surrounded by the rubble of neighbouring houses. Black smoke and fire conspired, turning dawn to dusk, an unending blackout. But amidst the tears and wreckage, a grim determination tempered with good humour, Jamie listened as he passed it all by.

"Ah looked oot ma windae and ah swear tae God, wee Jimmy Fleming wis sailin' doon the whisky river in a tin bath."

"Ye know whit she's like. Ye couldnae a dragged her away frae Burtons til she'd found a Yank tae pay fur that new jacket o hers. She wis still dancin' as the sirens were gaun."

And Jamie walked down to the river, dark as the smoke choked sky above, and he tossed the Golden Acorn into the waters, and it vanished into the black.

Already behind him, the clear up was well underway.

# URBAN MYTHS & LEGENDS

Official records show, that in the summer of 1942, the carcass of a large unidentified creature was washed up at Cardwell Bay. Council Officer Charles Rankin was sent to observe the badly decomposed remains.

"Measuring 27-28 ft. long, it had a lengthy neck, a relatively small flattened head with sharp muzzle and prominent eyebrow ridges, large pointed teeth in each jaw, rather large laterally sited eyes, a long rectangular tail that seemed to have been vertical in life, and two pairs of "L"-shaped flippers (of which the front pair were the larger, and the back pair the broader).

*Did The Clyde once play host to a creature like "Nessie"?*

The head was comparatively small, of a shape rather like that of a seal but the snout was much sharper and the top of the head flatter. The jaws came together one over the other and there appeared to be bumps over the eyes - say prominent eyebrows. There were large pointed teeth in each jaw. The eys were comparitively large, rather like those of a seal but more to the side of the head. Curiously, its body did not appear to contain any bones other than its spinal column, but its smooth skin bore many 6-inch-long, bristle-like 'hairs' - resembling steel knitting needles in form and thickness but more flexible."

Curiously, when Rankin cut open the besats stomach, he found "a small piece of knitted woollen material as from a cardigan" and even more bizarre, "a small corner of what had been a woven cotton tablecloth - complete with tassels". In Rankin's opinion, the remains were that of a huge lizard, however wartime restrictions permitted him from taking any photographs of the creature. He rang the Royal Scottish Museum in attempt to convince them to examine the creature, but the museum were not interested. Scientific examination of the creature would have been unlikely during the war years, there was simply no time for such work. Consequently, the beasts remains were hacked into pieces and subsequently buried beneath Saint Ninian's playing fields. However, Rankin removed one of the "knitting needle" bristles from the flipper of the creature, and he kept it for many years in his desk. It eventually shrivelled to resemble a finely coiled spring.

Cryptozoologists suggest that the creature may have been a basking shark, but agree that the large pointed teeth of the beast would tend to suggest it was in fact one of the carnivorous shark species. If it was indeed a carnivorous shark, then the size estimated by Rankin would actually make it one of the largest sharks ever discovered, for even Great Whites rarely exceed twenty feet in length. Rankin himself remained unconvinced by the "shark theory".

The mystery of "The Gourock Monster" was popularised in the late seventies when the story featured in an episode of "Arthur C. Clarke's Mysterious World". However no conclusions were reached as to the possible identity of the creature, and any possible answers still lie buried beneath the football pitch at Saint Ninians.

Gourock played host to another strange creature throughout the seventies and eighties, with numerous sightings of an enormous catlike creature. It was suggested that the animal was in fact a puma, similar to the "big cats" often sighted in the south of England. Indeed there are many recorded sightings of such black cats in and around Ayrshire at about the same time, however such sightings dwindled in the early nineties.

# Epilogue

## The Passing of the Torch

The water runs to meet the river from the hills high above the town.

On sunny days, you can walk along the waterways above Ravenscraig Forest and the Spango Glen and see better where the land meets the waves.

There is an Old Man lives up amongst the hills and moorland, and he watches over the town. He alone recalls how everything was, and he worries about how things will be. At nights, by moonlight, he writes down the old stories while he still can remember them.

And in a hollow by the waters edge, he keeps his museum. The hidden history of the town, up on the hill, under a little bridge.

A wolf pelt, a stone axe, the bones of Auld Dunrod, a tooth from Clutha the serpent, and more besides.

A magical history, always there, just where you cannot see it.

Walk then, with brave heart and open mind. Walk towards the future, glancing now and then over your shoulder to a past never truly gone. The journey will not end, and where you are headed matters not so much as that which you see and hear along the way. Unlike the castles now long since fallen, the past is not a fortress to be guarded, but rather a treasure to be shared.

So if you walk up on the hill and along Cornalees way, you may pass The Old Man as you look down upon the town. Be sure to smile and nod and he may tell you something you didn't know about life in the valley below. Perhaps he'll just remind you of something you've forgotten.

His walks grow shorter as the world grows older, and pieces from his museum disappear with each passing year, almost as if they were never there at all. When you meet him, listen, and remember what he has said. For every story, every song, is your own. And yours to give.

The Old Man is tired this autumn-purple evening; his steps are slow as he nears the bridge, nears the home of his treasures, the gifts he has gathered for longer than he cares to remember. He turns, once, as he nears his destination, to see the sun hang low on the water, and is filled with a feeling he cannot describe.

Once inside his museum, he is struck once again by the subtle changes around him; things have moved, faded somehow since he was last here.

He touches the objects gathered on the shelves of rock around him: what might be the tattered black robe of a monk; a stone shaped like a heart; a feather; a list of names; a gentleman's pipe long since extinguished. Sitting on a plinth above them all, his book.

He takes the volume down, his weary fingers running over the carved oak of its cover, familiar with every line. He opens. He reads. And these are the words he reads:

"Now there are many tales told of how Greenock came by its name..."

Magic torch would like to thank

National Lottery Heritage Board

Kate Robinson

Inverclyde Community Development Trust

Inverclyde Volunteer Centre

Ian Tarbet

Jim and Mairi Kelly

The staff of the Watt Library

Macintosh Family Archive

John McManus

Christopher Lee

All our proof readers

And all our friends and family

# Further Reading

| | |
|---|---|
| Adam | Witch Hunt - Scottish Witch Trials 1697 |
| Alexander & Steel | Wallace, Renfrewshire and The Wars Of Independence |
| Allen | Fingals Cave |
| Bolton | From Royal Stewart to Shaw Stewart |
| Brotchie | Scottish Western Holiday Haunts |
| Clarke | Mysterious World |
| Cockburn | The Celtic Church in Dunblane |
| Coughlan | Encyclopaedia of Arthurian Legends |
| Crawford | History of Renfrewshire |
| Douglas-Rhodes | Hills, Glens and Wicker Men |
| Frazer | The Golden Bough |
| Galt | Annals of the Parish |
| Geddes & Grosset | Celtic Mythology |
| Gibb | Much About Kilmacolm |
| Grant | The Lordship of the Isles |
| Hodge | Famous Trials |
| Lindsay | Lives of the Lindsays |
| MacPherson | The Poems of Ossian |
| Macrae | Notes About Gourock |
| Metcalfe | History of the County of Renfrew |
| Pennick | Celtic Saints |
| Sinclair | Statistical Account of Scotland (1791-1799) |
| Snoddy | Round About Greenock |
| Stewart & Matthews | Legendary Britain |
| Walker | South Clyde Estuary |